An Illustrated History of
Excavators

An Illustrated History of
Excavators

Hinton J. Sheryn

IAN ALLAN
Publishing

Acknowledgements

I would like to state that I owe a debt of gratitude to the numerous people and institutions who have all so kindly and freely given of their time and assistance. In addition, they have supplemented my lifetime collection of rare photographic material and without their contributions and permission this book would not have been possible. If any of the contributors have inadvertently been omitted then I can only offer sincere apologies and thank them for their invaluable help. In particular I would like to thank:

Peter N. Grimshaw (author of *Excavators* and *The Sunshine Miners*)

Joan Grimshaw

Peter Thomas Grimshaw

Bill Huxley (author of *Opencast Coal Plant & Equipment*)

John Honnor (Welland & Deeping Canal Commissioners)

Keith Haddock (Historical Construction Equipment Association)

David Stein (Canada)

Richard Lucas (Meldon Stone & Quarry Co, Okehampton, Devon)

Horace White (formerly of F. T. White & Sons, Newton Abbot, Devon)

Ron and Brenda Sismey (Corby, Northants)

Sue Bourne and David Ketteridge (Formerly of British Coal Opencast PR Dept)

Barry Cross (London Brick Company)

JCB (Uttoxeter)

Thomas W. Ward (Sheffield)

Richard & Mrs Ann Smalley (Smalley Excavators, Bourne, Lincolnshire)

The late John W. Page (USA)

Louis J. Cononelos (Director of Community Relations at Kennecott, Utah Copper)

Barber-Greene (a division of Caterpillar Paving Products Inc, DeKalb, Illinois, USA)

Walter F. Meinert (Advertising Manager of Barber-Greene)

Marion Power Shovel Company (Marion Indresco, USA)

Bucyrus-Erie (USA)

Link-Belt Speeder (USA)

Link-Belt (Italy, a division of FMC)

Thew-Lorain (USA)

Koehring (USA)

John Deere (USA)

International Harvester (USA)

J. I. Case (USA)

Baldwin Hamilton and Lima (USA)

Caterpillar Tractor Company (USA)

Warner-Swasey (USA)

P. & H. Harnischfeger (USA)

Frank F. Kobe (General Dynamics, USA)

O & K (Germany)

Weserhutte (Germany)

Backau-Wolf (Germany)

Poclain (Case & Poclain, France)

Liebher (France & Germany)

Norman Hill Plant Hire (London)

NCK-Rapier (formerly of Ipswich, Suffolk)

Mashinoexport (Moscow)

Mavor & Coulson (Glasgow)

Watts, Blake & Bearne (Clay & Minerals Co, Newton Abbot, Devon)

Mrs M. Magnusson & Associates (Royal Engineers' Library)

Leicester Museum of Science & Technology

Dyggor-Gaylord (CP Plant Holdings)

British Steel plc (Stewarts & Lloyds, United Steel Co)

Morrison Biggs Wall Ltd

Edward Gaskell & Jennie Marshall of Lazarus Co, Bideford, Devon, for help in preparation.

Dedicated to Caroline

Front cover: **JCB JS300LC.** *JCB*

Back cover: **The O & K RH120C** hydraulic excavator is among the most popular large-scale excavators of its type, working in iron-ore, gold, phosphate and coal mines and quarries throughout the world. This one is featured on an opencast coal mine in the North of England.

Back cover insets: **The Whitaker steam shovel made in 1884 in Leeds and a pre-war steam shovel at work in the china clay industry.** *English China Clays Group*

Title page: **One of the two huge Bucyrus-Erie 3850s that were made seen working at the River King Mine, Illinois (see page 59).** *F. Black*

First published 1995

ISBN 0 7110 2353 0

Published by Ian Allan Publishing

an imprint of Ian Allan Ltd, Terminal House, Station Approach, Shepperton, Surrey TW17 8AS.
Printed by Ian Allan Printing Ltd, Coombelands House, Coombelands Lane, Addlestone, Weybridge, Surrey KT15 1HY.

Contents

Picture Credits

All pictures are from the author's own collection with the exception of those on the following pages:
R. & B. Sismey: 11T, 16T, 19T, 19M, 19B, 20T, 21B, 30B, 39T, 39B, 40T, 57; Atlas Copco: 16M; English China Clays: 12B, 20B, 53T; Eisenwerk Weserhütte AG: 21T, 31T, 36T, 38R, 45M, 47, 54B, 55AR, 56B, 103B, 104TR, 104B; P. N. Grimshaw: 27B, 32T, 41T, 48AR, 61T, 61B, 69M, 76L; Link Belt SpA: 32B, 41B, 103T; Centrax Ltd: 34B; Hylton Warner & Co Ltd: 36B; NCK Rapier Ltd: 45T; A. Long & Co Ltd: 45B, 46T; G. Wimpey & Co: 46M; The Tank Museum: 52T; British Steel Corporation: 58T, 62T, 66B, 67B, 68T, 69T, 120T, 120B; F. Black: 59; Stewarts & Lloyds: 67T, 68B; I. Nicholas: 70; T. W. Ward Ltd: 81B, 82T, 101B; Norman Hill Plant Hire: 84T, 84B; Skye Agencies: 85M; K. Cooke/NCK Rapier Ltd: 85B; Ransomes & Rapier Ltd: 86T, 86M; NCK Rapier Ltd: 86B; Hodge Photos: 87T; A.R. Hawken: 88B; H. Baranger & Co: 90B; General Dynamics: 108; Krupp GmBH: 109T, 111T, 116B, 118B, 119T; Mavor & Coulson Ltd: 110T; Buckau R. Wolf AG: 111B, 112T, 112B, 113T, 113M, 113BL, 113BR, 114T, 114B, 115T, 118T; Orenstein & Koppel AG: 6–7, 114T, 114B, 115T, 118T; M. D. Smith Coast Co: 127T, 127B.

INTRODUCTION

For thousands of years man has been involved in large-scale earthmoving projects, for a wide variety of reasons. Some of the reasons are easily understood, many are still a mystery and the subject of debate in the high-tech 20th century.

The pyramids of Egypt are still the subject of much speculation, not so much for the reasons they were built, but more for how they were constructed by the Pharaohs 4,600 years ago.

The Great Wall of China is over 2,000 years old and is 2,000 miles long.

The linear earth boundaries of Nigeria, a product of the Benin Empire c1300BC, involved the removal of 100 million cu yd (75 million cu m) of earth.

In Dorset, England, 250,000cu yd (191,000cu m) of material was excavated in c1900BC for what is known as the Dorset Cursus.

The Greeks mined silver in the fourth and fifth centuries BC at Larium.

The Roman Empire was engaged in a whole host of large-scale civil engineering and mining projects, with the construction of roads, canals and

whole towns, while the mining of gold was under way in Italy and Spain before AD44. Their methods were primitive, relying on the masses of labour available to excavate and transport the soil. Tools made of flint, wood and iron were used for loosening and loading the material, which was then transported in wicker baskets or wooden carts. Animals such as mules, oxen, horses, camels and elephants were the hauliers of larger loads as they have been throughout the 18th and 19th centuries.

The American Indians discovered coal in out-

crops where workings dating from 1680 identify an early experiment with surface mining, where the overburden (strata of overlaying earth and rock) was removed using horse and mule-drawn ploughs. Crude scrapers were added to their inventory, as at Grape Creek in Danville, Illinois. In 1866 and in 1875 an opencast pit was worked at Hungary Hollow nearby. Anthracite seams in Pennsylvania were stripped in 1820, with wheelbarrows being the main earthmoving equipment used.

The extraction of minerals, fuel and clays together with the construction of canals and railways in the 1800s was still heavily reliant on hand labour, though a handful of pioneering engineers sensed that the time had come to consider the possibilities of mechanising the tough task of excavating earth, rock, clays and sand.

The first mechanical excavator was invented in Britain in 1796 when a 4hp James Watt steam engine was installed in a scow (or lighter) to operate dredging equipment. Later, in 1805, Oliver Evans produced similar dredges in the USA.

Dipper dredges had been in use in the very early years of the 19th century, when they were used to deepen harbours, canals and estuaries. Land versions, however, were not so successful, due largely to their lack of mobility. Being made almost entirely of wood, most simply fell to bits while digging or being moved. It was not until William Smith Otis, in the 1830s, felt the need to improve vastly on these early examples that the era of powered land excavators really began.

Left: **This O & K Wheel Excavator was photographed in July 1967 at a lignite mine. It was built by O & K of Germany.**

The author would like to emphasise that the status of manufacturers featured in this book may have changed since the date of the photographs used; as may their product line. He would like to apologise in advance for any offence that this inevitability may cause. In addition, the equipment featured in this book may not always be representative either of their products at the time or indeed their current status.

Single-Bucket Cable Type Excavators

SHOVELS

Otis

William S. Otis (born 1813) was living in Philadelphia, Pennsylvania, when he joined the contracting firm of Carmichael & Fairbanks in 1833. By 1834 he was a partner and helping to compete for contracts against the many other companies involved in the expansion of the railroads into the heart of the American Midwest.

One such contract had made Otis aware of the severe penalties involved if railroads were not operational on time, often including the loss of further lucrative orders. Moving the volume of earth involved in these operations was both slow and expensive, being done, save for a few horse-drawn dragpans and wagon-mounted graders, almost entirely by hand. It occurred to Otis that since steam engines had been in operation since the very early 1800s as rail or road locomotives (and stationary engines), it ought to be possible to utilise this technology to power the actions of a shovel.

Together with an engineering friend, Charles H. French, he designed and built the first steam-powered shovel at Canton in Massachusetts in 1835, where he had set up home. This prototype was soon hard at work on a major railroad construction project.

In 1836 Otis built a shovel using the engineering know-how and help of Garret & Eastwick. This was the first of many further shovels that went on to work during 1837. Otis's patent for the steam shovel was not accepted until early 1839. Meanwhile Garret had found that his rail and road locomotives had already been well received by operators and his interests were subsequently bought out by Joseph Harrison. The same year, William Otis died at the young age of 26.

In 1842, with a number of Otis shovels hard at work in North America, it is interesting to note that one was employed on a south of England railway contract, while another was *en route* to Russia to be joined by several more a year later.

Another rail construction engineer, who had known Otis, was to continue to produce Otis shovels in conjunction with John Souther. He was Oliver Chapman, and he, William Otis and John Souther paved the way for many more excavator manufacturers who emerged from the late 1800s both in the USA and Great Britain.

Machines were sold under the names Otis, Otis–Chapman, and Chapman–Souther. By 1880 several hundred machines had been manufactured and put to work. During this time many people, involved directly or indirectly with Otis, either as railroad engineers or as operators, had suggested modifications and improvements to these early shovels and over the following years there were numerous attempts at manufacturing improved steam-navvies.

Following in Otis's Footsteps

Following Otis's untimely death in 1839, the family were keen to see Otis Shovels survive. As a result, and following a subsequent marriage between Oliver Chapman and Otis's widow, the problem of patent law was overcome. Otis Shovels were then produced under the guidance of Oliver Chapman and John Souther.

In common with many of the new manufacturers of steam shovels in the late 1800s Ralph R. Osgood was experienced in their operation. So much so that he was able to identify areas in need of drastic improvements. Therefore, in 1875 and 1877, he

Above: **Picks, hand shovels, forks, iron bars, dibbers and wheelbarrows, with occasional help from horses, wagons and crude horse-drawn graders or pan scrapers, were the main tools of excavation for many decades before and even after the invention of mechanical steam shovels, scrapers or other machines.**

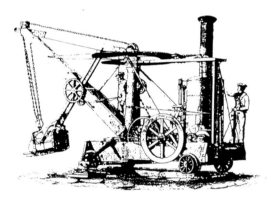

Left: The invention of the steam shovel by William Smith Otis pioneered a whole new industry which grew to mammoth proportions, with manufacturers gearing up for the challenge in many countries. Indeed many of the large surface-mining projects would not have been feasible without the use of powered excavators to move the millions of cubic yards of earth, rock and dirt to get at reserves of coal, phosphates, iron-ore or copper. The steam shovel, first invented in the 1830s, was slow to catch on elsewhere and another 30 or so years would pass before the glut of new manufacturers considered building such excavators. Then, within a very few years, many new USA, German, British, Swedish and Russian manufacturers (closely followed by Japanese and Chinese) were supplying steam-powered excavators to a wide variety of extraction and civil engineering companies.

patented his own shovels. As a result many more steam shovels began to see service not only on the railroads but on canal projects and the quarrying of minerals around the world. The Osgood range of shovels, draglines, backhoes and cranes continued to be produced until the company was acquired by Marion in the 1950s.

Hosea T. Stock was an experienced operator of Otis steam shovels himself before turning to the manufacture of his own brand in the later 1800s. Others included The Marion Steam Shovel Co of 1884 and Bucyrus (1882), both from the USA.

Left: The Thew portable steam shovel was among the earliest of USA excavators to incorporate full 360° slew and an alternative to rail lines. Introduced in 1895.

loaded into horse-drawn wagons. The hotel was built to 14 storeys and contained 350 apartments.

In 1911 Marion produced one of the earliest purpose-built stripping shovels for the mining industry.

A complete line of contractor-size universal excavators was produced in vast numbers through to the early 1960s, when they concentrated solely on mining shovels and draglines and a hydraulic excavator.

After 50 or so years of stripping-shovel production, Marion received an order for the largest shovel ever built, the 6360-M (see *Stripping Shovels*). The first Marion walking dragline was built in 1939; the 7200-M was still working late into the 1980s, 50 years after its commisioning (see *Walking Draglines*).

The contractor-size machines from the 1940s and 1950s ranged from ¾cu yd 33–M, 1cu yd 43–M (of which over 450 were made by 1962), the 45 and 47, 362, through to the 111-M of 4½cu-yd capacity, up to the line of electric and diesel-electric shovels and draglines of between 5 and 45cu yd-plus capacity for the largest 301-M shovel. Marion having acquired the Osgood Company, also took control of the Quickway Crane & Shovel Co of Denver.

Marion's only real challenger is Bucyrus-Erie. They, like Marion, built a massive range of construction-size excavators and cranes, walking draglines, mining shovels, draglines and stripping shovels. They also made a range of bucket-wheel excavators.

Marion

For well over a century, Marion have held the undoubted distinction of being one of the two largest manufacturers of excavating equipment in the world. Yet their early entry into the steam shovel business was brought about through the need to speed up their railroad building programmes, and in response to the vast interest being shown in mechanical excavators by the world's mining companies, canal building engineers, brick companies, quarries and the like. Overall, a tremendous market awaited those prepared to manufacture these huge shovels. One steam shovel operator, Henry Barnhart, felt he had enough experience of such machines to produce excavators with the help of others. George King and Edward Huber were similarly persuaded, and they joined forces to produce the Marion steam shovel at the Huber factory in Marion, Ohio, which produced a range of agricultural machines and eventually compaction equipment, rollers, etc.

Marion Steam Shovel Co was born in 1884. In 1900, it was decided to invest in their own factory, again in Marion, from which a very large number of steam shovels would emerge, destined for mines throughout North America, Europe and Central America, where 24 of their shovels were to assist in the digging of the massive canal in Panama, which would unite the Pacific and Atlantic oceans.

At the iron-ore quarries of the Midlands in England, two Marion shovels helped remove the iron-ore and limestone in such demand in British industry.

In Canada, the mining of all manner of minerals and fuels provided a very substantial market for Marion, while the major construction projects were also interested in using steam shovels. The Fort Garry Hotel in Winnipeg required a massive excavation for the basement and foundations. Much of the earthmoving was undertaken by a very early dragline and a Marion steam shovel. The spoil was

Bucyrus

From the manufacturing of equipment for the railroads to becoming one of the largest excavator manufacturers on earth, Bucyrus has come a long way since it manufactured its first steam shovel in 1882. Again, this was for a railroad company in Ohio, USA.

By 1894 over 170 Bucyrus machines were at work. By 1911, it had joined forces with both the Vulcan Steam Shovel Co and the Atlantic Steam Shovel & Equipment Co. Between the three of them they were able to supply shovels for rail and mining applications in many countries.

As early as 1894 Bucyrus machines were being supplied in very large numbers to individual contracts such as the Chicago Drainage Channel where

Right: The Wilson Number One steam navvy supplied to the ironstone quarries of Northamptonshire, England, in 1895, was an early example of a British-built excavator having 360° slew. Made in Liverpool by John Wilson & Co.

Below right: The Ruston-Dunbar steam shovels were first introduced in 1875 and a very large number were produced for work as varied as mining, quarrying and the construction of canals and railways; as seen in this photograph taken on the Great Central Railway project in Nottingham, England, between 1895 and 1898.

24 of a total of 54 machines were supplied by Bucyrus. In the early years of the 20th century the massive Panama Canal project had taken delivery of no less than 77 Bucyrus machines, to add to their stock of 24 Marions and a solitary Thew shovel. At the same time as the Panama order, 18 Bucyrus machines were sent to a copper mine in Spain, while yet more were heading for iron-ore excavations in North America and ironstone mines in the English Midlands.

The Erie Steam Shovel Co of Erie, Pennsylvania was acquired by Bucyrus in 1927, even though the Erie order books were full at the time and their machines were hard at work both in the USA and England. Three years later Bucyrus joined forces with the Ruston Co of England to form what became known as Ruston Bucyrus.

The fact that Bucyrus machines were being produced from their Milwaukee, Wisconsin, factory from 1893, and in Canada (under licence) from 1904, as well as in Russia (again under licence) from 1900 and Great Britain from 1930 made them a powerful manufacturer and difficult competitor. The only company who could possibly match their productive capabilities was Marion. This, of course, did not stop a string of new competitors from entering the fray: Manitowoc from around 1925, NorthWest from 1921, P & H from the 1920s, Unit from 1925, Koehring, 1922, Insley from 1924, Link Belt Speeder, 1922, The American (under various guises) from 1904 and Bay City from 1913. All of these companies were North American. From elsewhere in the USA came the challenges of Allis-Chalmers, Badger, Little Giant, Stardrill-Keystone and others. Many amalgamated into larger companies, some closed down,

while others produced excavators of one sort or another for many more years. In the case of Allis-Chalmers, they continued to produce a wide range of agricultural and earthmoving machines for many years, before finally joining forces with Fiat of Italy.

Thew-Lorain

Early in the 1890s Capt Richard P. Thew commanded an ore boat on the Great Lakes. His job was to pick up iron-ore from the fields of Lake Superior and deliver it to the steel mills near Cleveland on Lake Erie.

The contract under which he worked specified a delivery quota for the season with bonus payments for every additional load. This incentive was so attractive to both captain and crew that they became impatient with the inadequate unloading facilities at the various docks. Several days of delay while they awaited their turn to unload was both common and costly. The rail-mounted shovels used in the stevedoring were slow, inflexible and often destructive to both docks and equipment. Working 'over-one-end'

Left: The **Whitaker** steam shovel was the pioneer of the fully revolving steam shovel, made in **1884** by **Whitakers of Leeds in Yorkshire.** It is seen here hard at work on railway contracts.

Below left: The china clay industry of Southwest England was once a conglomeration of privately-owned clay pits and kilns, where much of the overburden was removed by manual labour for many years – well into the years approaching World War 2. Labour was cheap and plentiful. The more adventurous companies did, however, invest in steam shovels. One such machine is featured in this photograph, and is very similar to a steam shovel which stood on the edge of a disused clay pit on the edge of Dartmoor up until the mid-1950s, although it had ceased work prior to World War 2, when the clay pit was closed.

(limited slew) and with a boom that had no horizontal crowd and very limited lateral movement, these machines served only to spur Thew on, in sheer frustration, to draw up plans for a greatly improved specification. These rough drawings, which Thew was convinced would revolutionise ore handling, he took along to machine and metal-working shops in Cleveland, Ohio.

His new shovel rolled on wide, steel wheels, had a full 360° slew, was able to dig and deliver material from any position and had a horizontal crowding movement which enabled it to reach in for loads without causing the damage so common with previous shovels.

In 1859, Thew approached one of the steel companies and offered to unload their ore at an unbelievably low price. The company concerned did so well from the deal that they bought Thew's shovel. This left him free to concentrate on building further shovels, all of which were purchased by the various steel companies.

By 1899 he had sold shovels to all of the steel com-

panies around, which meant that he needed to look further afield for alternative markets. However, this proved less of a problem than his need of help in production. This was solved when Thew teamed up with F. A. Smythe, an Elyria, Ohio, businessman. Together they formed the Thew Automatic Shovel Co Inc in 1899. Matthew Andrews and Silas Hitchcock (both of Cleveland); and E. M. Pierce and W. O. Donaldson (both of Lorain) completed a six-man board of directors. From then on, Thew shovels were finding new markets in mines, brickworks, canals, and general excavation for buildings and highways. In 1903 a new product was marketed with outstanding success — a full 2cu yd-capacity railroad swing-boom machine.

In the same year Thew shovels were being offered with a single electric motor. Other electrically-powered shovels of that period had individual motors for each and every machine function — the Thew operated all motions, via a gearing train, from just one motor.

The original Thew shovels were made in various workshops and factory sites in and around Cleveland, Ohio. By 1907 all production was centred in a completely new unit in Lorain. From 1917 Lorain was added to the Thew name. All subsequent machines were known around the world as the Lorain. This became the industry standard, with many USA com-

panies adopting the names of their town of origin, for example: Bucyrus, Marion and Lima (Ohio), Bay City (Michigan) and many more.

In 1917, the USA entered World War 1. Much of the production of Lorain and other companies was destined to cross the Atlantic in an effort to help the Allies. Many manufacturers were encouraged to diversify into products aimed entirely at the war effort. A shortage of dockside (mobile) cranes, which were urgently required in the unloading of desperately needed equipment, caused Thew to develop a crane mounted on steel wheels. This could then be towed to its required position by dockside trucks and lorries.

A real need was for a 5-ton crane mounted on a truck chassis fitted with rubber tyres. F. A. Smythe of Thew-Lorain successfully designed and produced just such a crane, though by the time of its full production in 1919 the war had ended. Smythe went on to form the International Crane Co, a direct subsidiary of Thew-Lorain. In addition, they formed the Universal Crane Co, set up to lease out cranes on an international basis. They were the first company to set up such a venture.

It was in 1920 that the Model Type O crawler shovel with dippers (buckets) ranging from ⅔ to ⅝cu yd-capacity with a 25ft boom first appeared, along with a type 00 (¾cu yd-capacity) and the A1 at 1¼cu yd.

Thew-Lorain built its last steam-powered shovel in the 1920s. From then on all new models were available with the option of gasoline, diesel or electric power.

Above: **This Marion model 36–E was one of the first Marion machines to have been fitted with crawler tracks, and was electrically powered. Marion steam shovels crossed the Atlantic to work in the ironstone mines of the Midlands, while 24 Marion steam shovels worked alongside 77 Bucyrus and one solitary Thew steam shovel on the massive Panama Canal project between 1904 and 1914.**

In 1925 a new crawler-mounted shovel of 1¼cu yd, with a 40ft boom and a 12ft minimum working radius was introduced. It was so successful that orders were fast outstripping the production capacity of the factory. A new company was formed to provide extra castings, and a new machine named the Lorain 75 was to prove their most successful excavator.

Dramatic new changes were to take place over the next few years. The USA was to suffer an economic collapse sparked off by the Wall Street crash of October 1929, and this was to have repercussions throughout the industrialised world. Lorain, having spent huge amounts of capital on their bold expansion programme, looked as vulnerable as any of the hundreds of other companies who eventually ended up in liquidation. Their direct sales system, under which Lorain were financing all machines other than those sold on a cash basis, was to add to their troubles. Many of the original directors had died, leaving only F. A. Smythe to take responsibility. Fortunately his good business knowledge, which had

Above: **The Bucyrus 70c featured here is similar to those 70-ton and 90-ton Bucyrus steam shovels which moved record amounts of earth, rock and dirt on the Culebra Cut section of the Panama Canal *c*1908.**

proved its worth in the past, was sufficient to see them through, and Lorain continued even if only on a reduced production basis. It was mainly the high sales achieved by the Lorain 75, along with other new products of the 1920s, that were to prove the saviours of the company.

One of these new products was developed shortly after the 75. It was a special excavator made for use in underground mines and tunnels. Of the 90 or so that were built, no less than 50 were shipped to work in the mining area around St Joseph, Missouri. These were so successful that many were still at work well into the 1960s. Having no boom at all, only a horizontal scoop, they were the miners' best friend.

A few years prior to the market's collapse, a new destination was found for Lorain excavators with the opening up of the state of Florida. Plans for railways, highways, hotels and houses meant that access to this largely forgotten state became vital to the needs of tourism and business alike. The state was also rich in minerals such as phosphates, and before

long literally hundreds of Lorain shovels were heading southeast. Compare this with the stark contrast of 1933 when the grand total of machines sold for the whole year was just six.

Following the crash, Lorain continued by introducing a new line of products on to the markets, including the all-new Moto-Crane. A complete line of these was produced and gained the distinction of being firsts for the industry on two counts. They were the only machines to be built fitted on to the company's own carrier. Also, they were the largest and most capable machines ever to be mounted on rubber tyres. They could be equipped as cranes or shovels. The smallest (the MC-2) carried a bucket capacity of ½cu yd, and a lift of 17,000lb weight. The two larger machines (the MC-3 and the MC-4) handled buckets of ¾cu yd, and could lift weights of 22,000lb and 30,000lb respectively.

These machines were incorporated into the company's lease-lend division (Universal Crane Co) and brought in valuable capital. During World War 2 they were fitted with 240mm howitzers and sent to the front lines. Once again, Thew-Lorain products were to assist in a war effort, this time equipped as fighting machines.

Above: **Note the wood pile at the rear of this Bucyrus
Steamer working on an iron-ore mining contract
while its somewhat older assistant removes the
overburden. The wood pile is fuel for the steam
engines.**

Above right: **The Atlantic Steam Shovel Co became part of the giant Bucyrus organisation in 1911, as did the Vulcan Steam Shovel Co. This Atlantic steam shovel crossed the Atlantic to work on the Calcine Bank in Corby. This type 45 is photographed working for the steel companies in 1930, though is likely to have been at work there much earlier.**

Centre right: **Atlas Copco, known throughout the world for their compressed air and mining equipment, were given an order for four steam shovels to work on the state railways of Sweden in 1911. This photograph shows one of the four.**

Below: **An early Erie type 'B' Railroad Ditcher steam shovel from the 1920s.**

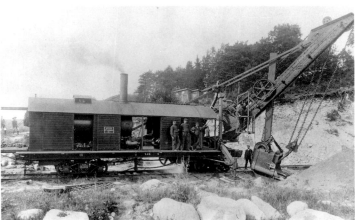

Above: **This Bucyrus 80B** electrically-powered shovel from 1925 must surely be an indicator that from these very early years of excavator development the machines were indeed growing in stature.

Right: **The Model 'A' Erie** full-slew steam shovel was made originally by the Ball Engineering Co, who had -specialised previously in stationary steam engines. Erie merged with Bucyrus in 1927 to create one of the largest excavator manufacturers in the world.

Above: **This Bucyrus 50B steam shovel working for a coal mining company in 1928 is another example of the scaling up of excavators.**

Right: **The Weserhutte L8 steam shovel was the first of a long line of excavators to be produced by Weserhutte of Bad Oeynhausen, Germany, from 1908 — just four years after the first German-made steam shovel made its début.**

Right: This 12-ton Ruston steam shovel seen working at Easton Neston for Towcester Mineral & Brick Co in the Midlands, England, is one of hundreds of similar machines manufactured at Ruston's of Lincoln for work at home and abroad.

This announcement was made in *Quarry Management* magazine in August 1922:

'*We are pleased to say that Messrs. Ruston & Hornsby Ltd have just received an order from the Public Works Department, New Zealand for two exceptionally large dragline excavators, mounted on Caterpillar Travelling Gear, and fitted with 65ft jib and buckets of two cubic yards capacity. Very strong competition was experienced from the best known American makers of excavating machinery. A further contract has also been received for a No 10 Crane Navvy, with a 1½ cubic yard bucket and mounted on Caterpillar Travelling Gear, for the New Plymouth Harbour Board, New Zealand.*'

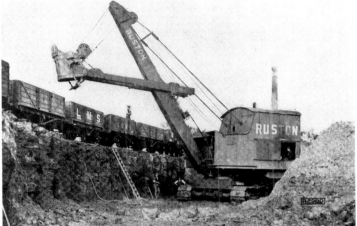

Centre right: The ironstone mines of the Midlands were valued customers for the manufacturers of excavating equipment on both sides of the Atlantic. Here is a Ruston 20-ton steam shovel, made in Lincoln, working at the steel company's Cranford quarries.

Left: This Ruston No 4 type shovel is loading limestone at Longhills Progress in the ironstone/limestone belt of the Midlands. In fact, many of the early steam shovels were still at work well into the 1950s; this photo was taken in 1953.

Above: **This 20-ton Ruston is loading a conveyor transporter at Lowick in Northamptonshire.**

Left: **This crawler-mounted Ruston steam shovel is loading rock from the face of a quarry.**

Below left:
This unique Bucyrus limited-slew excavator is removing overburden at a Cornish china clay pit in the 1930s.

Above right: **This Weserhutte type LR4 is loading rock into a very early haul-truck in the 1930s at a German quarry.**

Right: **A view of the quarry at Preston's-Pit Progress in Northampton on 8 October 1953. The old Ruston Steamer is still hard at work several decades after its manufacture. In common with other steam shovels made in the early years of this century, such as the Bucyrus steam shovels which went to work in a copper mine in Spain as early as 1904, many were still at work in the mid-1950s. The availability of wood and coal for fuel was one factor which kept them going, whereas electricity and oil was not as widely available in, for example, the Andalusian mines at that time. Still, there is little doubt that the old shovels were made to last. A Weserhutte L8 (one of the first to be made in 1908) was still hard at work in a German quarry in 1968 and no doubt for some time after.**

Above left: **The first steam shovel of the Utah Copper Co at their Bingham Canyon Mine near Salt Lake City was a 2.5cu yd steam shovel, mounted on railway tracks, and was a limited slew machine which started work in 1906. It began by mining the surface of a mountain of low grade copper-ore.**

Left: In 1925 new 4.5cu yd-capacity steam shovels started carving out those benches so familiar in copper mines. Although still incorporating limited slew, they had progressed to travelling on their own tractor-type crawlers.

Above: **By 1947 the shovels had progressed to capacities of 7cu yd. They were crawler-mounted, fully revolving and electrically powered. In this picture a shovel is loading ore into a rail car for shipment to the Bingham Canyon concentrator 15 miles away.**

Above: **In 1961 the electric shovels at Bingham Canyon had 8cu yd dippers capable of scooping up 16 tons of material in one pass. This shovel is loading waste rock that covers the ore body into side-dumping rail cars.**

Right: **King-size electric shovels with 34cu yd dippers scoop 70 tons of material (equal in weight to about 35 large cars) in a single bite. The shovel shown here is loading a 240-ton capacity diesel haul-truck. For a comparison of size, look for the 6ft-tall man standing at the rear of the shovel in this photograph taken in 1994. It is little wonder after all these years that Bingham Canyon is so large a man-made hole in the ground that it can be seen from outer space.**

Below: **An early 19 R–B excavator is seen here equipped with a weighing device for loading quarried rock in exact amounts on to a truck, in a quarry near Okehampton on Dartmoor in 1939. This British Rail-owned quarry has been responsible for supplying railway ballast for most of the rail network in Britain over most of this century. It also supplies quarry products to the civil engineering and road construction industries.**

Right: This electric 54 R–B shovel is seen with a full dipper load at the Cornelly Quarry in May 1949.

Below: This early 1950s 10 R–B is busy in a ball clay pit, in Newton Abbot, Devon. It is one of almost 8,000 to have been made at the Lincoln works before the end of the 1960s.

Left: The opencast coal industry in Great Britain (like the ironstone mines of the Midlands) used a wide variety of excavators. This Ruston-Bucyrus 21 R–B shovel (foreground) is helping its partner, a 24 R–B, to recover coal at the Shotton opencast coal site in the north of England in 1944.

Centre left: A USA-made Bucyrus 55, 2cu yd shovel (on the left) and a Lima 1201, (again made in the USA) 2.5cu yd-capacity shovel are in this photograph ably assisted by two Caterpillar D8 tractors and a D4. Amazingly there appears to be little difference in their size. Compare these with the huge D8 tractors of today where current models would make these shovels look small. In 1944 at this Northumberland opencast coal site they were state of the art.

Below: A Royal visit to an opencast coal site in 1944 must have been a great day for the operators of this early steam shovel and the little steam railway engine. A pioneering coal site, the surface mine at Wentworth was one of the British coal industry's major contributions to the nation's energy requirements for some years to come.

Left: Ransomes & Rapier of Ipswich in Suffolk were granted a patent for their rope crowd gear in 1914 which quickly became a standard feature on their own contractor-size shovels and on many of their competitors' machines.

The 4½ models, however, did not use a crowd system but, like other very small shovels of the 1940s and 1950s, used a 'luffing' shovel attachment whereby the main boom was raised and lowered to give the shovel bucket the necessary amount of reach into the bank. This was also used on the model 410 Ransomes & Rapier machine, but in this case a full crowd mechanism was also available as an option.

Full crowd means that the dipper handle is allowed to slide in and out of the boom, enabling it to reach all points of the bank, without having to raise or lower the main boom. In this photograph the little 4½ demonstrates the 'luffing' shovel.

Centre left: In this photograph a model 410 from Ransomes & Rapier is also using a 'luffing' shovel to load a lorry in the mid-1940s.

Below left: In this photograph the Rapier 410 is equipped with Rapier's patent rope crowd shovel equipment.

Above right: This NCK 304 shovel loading coal at a British opencast coal site has caused problems for the Bedford truck. Help is at hand from the little Allis-Chalmers bulldozer.

Right: When bought new in 1962 this NCK 605 shovel was destined for a large quarry in the Ashburton area of Devon. It could not have arrived at a better time for the contractors working on the Exeter bypass, as it was necessary to cut through a very high bank to facilitate building of a large roundabout. It was one of the few large shovels in the area capable of reaching the deep red clay bank, with the help of a fleet of Foden dump trucks. These trucks had been hired out to the main contractor by Western Excavating Company of St Austell in Cornwall, where they would normally have been found hauling 'stent' (sand and decomposed granite waste) from the deep clay pits for the parent company English China Clay.

Left: **This large NCK 1405 shovel makes short work of loading an 8-ton haul-truck, a Heathfield, made locally to the Ashburton quarry in Newton Abbot in Devon. Other quarries operated by Glendinnings were in Dorset.**

Below left: **This NCK-Rapier 304 shovel, loading an ageing haul-truck is in a Lyme Regis quarry in Dorset in the early 1950s.**

Below: **A Blaw-Knox BK50 fitted with face shovel and hard at work for the Royal Engineers.**

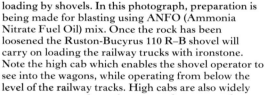

Below: **Even some of the world's biggest excavators** require some help in loosening dense rock and clay formations which have lain undisturbed for millions of years. This help can come from blasting or ripping using large crawler tractors equipped with long ripper teeth. These can tear apart the ground to depths of 3 or 4ft, and by cross ripping a whole area can be made ready for bulldozing over the edge of a face ready for

loading by shovels. In this photograph, preparation is being made for blasting using ANFO (Ammonia Nitrate Fuel Oil) mix. Once the rock has been loosened the Ruston-Bucyrus 110 R–B shovel will carry on loading the railway trucks with ironstone. Note the high cab which enables the shovel operator to see into the wagons, while operating from below the level of the railway tracks. High cabs are also widely used on other types of excavator, for example those using crane and grabbing equipment on wharves and docks, where the operator has to be able to see into the holds of ships; in scrap yards when stacking old cars or feeding a bailer, or even when equipped with logging grapples for the handling of large logs and timber either in the forests, the stacking yards or the docks. Many of the large electric shovels loading coal from seams into very large haul-trucks require the operator to be well on top of the main machinery house of the shovel in order to see clearly into the haul-truck when loading.

Above: **The Weserhutte W1600 shovel in this**
photograph shows its unique dipper release
mechanism, which normally consists of a single rope-
operated latch. When the rope is pulled, the latch
releases to swing open the trapdoor, which is
suspended by two hinges. On the W1600, two ropes
slide the whole bottom away from the opening in the
bottom of the bucket. This shovel also features a rope
crowd mechanism. It was in operation from the 1940s
and was the largest of the Weserhutte range
(represented by the W300 to this, the W1600). Much
larger excavators were to follow in the late 1950s and
1960s.

Below: The Lima 2400 was without doubt one of the
most popular excavators in the 4–7cu yd range,
equipped either as shovel or dragline. Many worked
on British opencast coal sites. It was the largest of
Lima's line of excavators and first appeared in 1928.

Baldwin-Lima-Hamilton were makers of a wide
range of construction and railway engineering
products, which included graders and hydraulic
cranes. When the group was acquired by Clark (makers of the Michigan range of wheel loaders, scrapers
and wheel bulldozers) these were also added to the
range of construction equipment. Clark were also
excavator manufacturers in their own right, with a line
of small contractor-size crawler- and truck-mounted
machines. Many of these were assembled under
licensing agreements in Britain by Allen of Oxford.
Likewise the USA Lima excavators were also made in
the UK by locomotive manufacturers in the north of
England. As with most excavator manufacturers, it is
at times difficult to be quite sure how they arrive at the
model numbers.

Lima, for example, made machines with the
number 34 (I can remember seeing one at Barry
Docks, in South Wales, in the early 1960s — it was
powered by a Caterpillar D4 engine — complete, on
that occasion, with crane equipment. It may well have
been waiting for its last move to the scrap yard). Other
Lima models included the 802, 901, 1201 and the 2400.
No doubt there were others which are not represented
in this list.

Marion, meanwhile, produced the models 33–M,
43, 45, 47, 63, 93, 101 and 111–M, but other models in
between these size ranges included the 362.

Whatever the methods of choosing their numbers,
there is little doubt that Marion and Lima were
amongst the major manufacturers of excavating
equipment for the surface mining and civil
engineering industries. Sadly, Marion no longer
produce contractor-size machines, though their
mining excavators are impressive and still popular the
world over. Lima ceased trading some years ago,
although a number of Lima draglines and a few
shovels are still hard at work in surface mining
operations in Britain and elsewhere.

Left: The Smith 21 shovel was one of the most popular ¾cu yd excavators to emerge from British manufacturers. Around 19 units, equipped with dragline and shovel, were used extensively in the removal of waste sand and rock from the clay pits of Devon and Cornwall. Others were used as coal-loading shovels at opencast mines in the UK, and on construction sites. It was powered by a Gardner diesel engine and featured the twin dipper stick with rack and pinion crowd. Other Smith excavators included the Super 8 and Super 10 during the 1940s and 1950s. Later models included the Smith 26, available as shovel, dragline or crane; the Eurocrane, for dragline, grab and crane duties; and the E1400 or E2800 — both basically crane/dragline models.

Below: The Link-Belt Speeder DS-408 is one of the Link-Belt shovel models which was available from their factories in North America, Italy, Japan and Mexico. The machine featured here is working in the USA.

Above: The little Soviet model E–652A shovel loading this truck at a Middle Eastern construction site in 1969 is just one of a very large range of Soviet-designed and built excavators. They worked on construction, quarrying and mining sites around the world, for example in India, the Middle East, Spain and Eastern Europe.

Below: This Soviet-built electric mining shovel is the E–2503 from the mid– to late–1960s.

Above: **In the ironstone quarries of the Midlands this electric Ransomes & Rapier shovel has no problem loading the Euclid R–30 haul-truck with heavy ironstone. The model 4142, though made in the 1950s, was still at work up until the UK ironstone mining industry finally closed its operations in the early 1970s.**

Right: **A 30 R–B shovel loading a Heathfield haul-truck at a quarry near Torquay in South Devon during the 1960s/1970s. The 30 R–B was one of the earlier models to be equipped with full air control, easing the efforts of operators, whose arms must have had the muscles of a weight-lifter after pushing and pulling those manual levers all day. The Priestman Lion Mk111 was one of that company's first machines to become air controlled during the early 1960s.**

The Heathfield haul-truck was made at the Centrax Factory in Newton Abbot before, on joining forces with Haulamatic, Heathfield transferred their operations to the West Midlands to form Unipower Haulamatic-Heathfield Ltd.

Right: The Bucyrus-Erie **88B** is one of the most advanced shovels of its kind. This one is working on a British opencast coal site. The series IV was introduced in 1982, but the original model **88–B** made its début in 1946.

Below: This Marion **101–M** is equipped with Marion's revolutionary Superfront shovel attachment. This equipment has been widely accepted around the world on much larger electric mining shovels. Thirteen such machines were sold for mining operations in Russia, copper mines in the remote mountains of Papua New Guinea, coal mining in Australia, and mining in North America.

   Machines such as the Marion **194–M** and the **204–M** are able to handle buckets to 30cu yd-plus capacity. This **101–M** electrically-powered excavator was the prototype for this equipment, and after working in numerous USA coal mines, returned to work at a limestone quarry not too far from the Marion factory in Ohio.

Right: This large Weserhutte shovel made in Germany from the mid-1960s is one of the last of the heavy-duty cable-operated shovels from Weserhutte, whose excavators began in the steam era in 1908.

Below: This Marion 182-M, one of many to have worked at British opencast coal mines, is equipped with a 10cu yd dipper and powered through Ward-Leonard electric control and makes short work of loading the 100-ton dump truck. This excavator was made in the UK by Marion's manufacturing concessionaire Babcock & Wilcox.

    This Babcock-Marion 182–M is working at the Llanilid opencast coal site in Glamorgan, South Wales, during the early 1980s.

DRAGLINES

Left: The first practical dragline machine was devised by John W. Page in 1903.

Below: Another form of dragline was that operated from a portable steam tractor, such as this one used by contractors Mounement & Day at the Witham Forth District, north of Boston in Lincolnshire *c*1920.

Above: **This steam dragline is a Class 7 from Bucyrus.** Note it is typical of the draglines of this period, having been mounted on heavy wooden sleepers and moving on sets of steel rollers.

Below: **This Ransomes & Rapier crawler dragline is busy working for the Middle Level Commissioners in 1940 in the East Midlands.**

Right: **This model LM 9.5 from Weserhutte in Germany was one of their popular draglines from the 1930s period.**

Left: **This Ruston No 4 is working on the removal of stones and boulders on Earlstrees Restoration on 15 September 1952 following ironstone mining.**

Below: **This dragline is at work in the Earlstrees Quarry of the Midlands ironstone industry in June 1949.**

Above: **The two draglines working here are a Ruston-Bucyrus 54 R–B (right) and a Lima 1201, at the Park Lodge North site in the ironstone mines during October 1954.**

Left: **This is a USA Lorain dragline working at the Shotton opencast coal site near Newcastle in 1944.**

Above right: **The Smith 21 dragline here is one of many which worked on construction sites and in mining throughout Britain during the 1950s and 1960s. Smith 21s were also made under licensing agreements in India.**

Right: **These two Link-Belt Speeder LS–98 draglines are examples of very popular excavators which were produced in four factories around the world, in Italy, Mexico, Japan and the USA. This pair were at work in the late 1960s.**

Right: The Ransomes & Rapier 410 on dragline duties. This model was first produced in the 1940s.

Below: This little Ruston-Bucyrus 10 R–B is removing overburden at a ball clay pit in Devon in the 1950s. Note the Muir-Hill dumper which the 10 R–B is loading. These were very widely used in the clay industry well into the 1960s.

Left: This is one of many Priestman Lion Mk 111 excavators employed by ball and china clay producer Watts, Blake & Bearne of Newton Abbot in Devon. These machines were employed at the company's works in Newton Abbot as well as their clay pits on the southern edge of Dartmoor. In earlier years WBB used the Priestman Wolfe, Tiger and earlier series of the Lion. This photograph was taken around 1964 although the machines were still in use well into the 1980s. Note the 'goosenecked' dumper which the dragline is about to load with sand.

Below: The Marion 93–M dragline (here using a Hendrix perforated bucket) was made in India well into the mid-1980s and possibly a lot later. Designed and built originally by the Marion Power Shovel Co of Marion, Ohio it weighed around 70 tons and could handle buckets of 3cu yd-capacity with ease.

Left: This is a Link-Belt Speeder LS–318, working in December 1970 on a flood prevention scheme.

Below left: The skill of dragline operators is here tested to the full, in swinging a big bucket towards a relatively small truck. There are two Northwest draglines in this photograph, the front one being a model 95.

Above right: The NCK Rapier 605B dragline was a formidable machine from the company in Sheffield, England, which made machines under licence to the Koehring Company of the USA. They had gained valuable experience producing earlier machines under a similar agreement with Harnischfeger Corporation, which make the machines which carry the P & H logo.

This particular dragline is at a sand and gravel operation in Hertfordshire, England, during the early 1970s.

Above: This big Weserhutte W180 dragline has all the appearance of the very latest and perhaps last of a long line of excavators from the notable German manufacturer. Made from 1964 through to around the 1970s.

Left: One of the most popular USA-made draglines to enter British opencast coal sites in later years is the Manitowoc 4600, which first appeared in 1961 as Manitowoc sought to upgrade their model 4500. Known as the Vicon because of its variable power control system, the 7.5cu yd-capacity dragline has worked for many of the well known opencast coal contractors on a variety of sites in Britain. Millions of cubic yards of overburden removal is a tribute to its achievements in the USA on sites from Pennsylvania to Florida.

Above: This Manitowoc is digging deep at a coal mine in Yorkshire, England, in the early 1980s, though it is more than likely still in operation well into the 1990s.

Right: This is the Marion 195–M crawler dragline working for a major opencast coal contractor, George Wimpey & Co. It has to be the largest crawler dragline to have operated on a site in Britain.

Having a weight of some 550 tons, bucket capacities of between 13 and 17cu yd and booms to 170ft, this machine would dwarf many of the early walking-draglines such as the Ransomes & Rapier W–80 or the Ruston-Bucyrus 5–W.

Below right: The dragline featured here is somewhat different from others shown in that its carrier is a six-wheel truck and is being operated by the Royal Engineers of the British Army. Blaw-Knox (one of the very earliest manufacturers of bulldozer blades, scrapers and graders) manufactured this, the BK50, which was also available on tracks and as a universal excavator. It could handle all the usual front-end equipment such as shovel, backacter, skimmer, dragline, grab and crane. It is shown here in travelling position with its bucket mounted just in front of the excavator cab, on the carrier.

BACKHOES

The backhoe (sometimes known as the backacter, dragshovel or hoe) has become the most popular form of excavator attachment for contractor-size machines and in many instances is used on mining machines, although in almost all cases hydraulic excavators are used. For cable type backacters one can go back to around the turn of the century and beyond and find early experiments of this type of equipment. It is best suited for the digging of trenches, and is also a very useful tool for stripping topsoil,

overburden, tarmac and for exposing and loading minerals such as coal seams. Some of the examples used here are fitted to the universal excavator as one of the four or five optional front ends. The main boom was often available either as a straight or a 'gooseneck' type, the latter allowing for a much deeper dig.

Below: **The Weserhutte Type LR4 excavator from Germany loading little side-tipping wagons during the 1920s.**

47

Above: **The Rapier 4.5** excavator with dragshovel on a straight boom, and a bucket which could itself be used as a face shovel, skimmer or dragshovel. This was used during the late 1940s and throughout the 1950s.

Right: The Smith 21 universal excavator with dragshovel on a 'gooseneck' type boom was popular throughout the 1950s and 1960s.

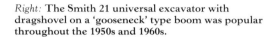

Above right: **The Northwest 25–D** dragshovel was one of the many contractor-size universal excavators from North America that helped bring about the growth of the infrastructure as we know it today, with large sewer, water, gas and oil pipelines to feed the towns and cities of the USA, Canada and elsewhere. Thousands of miles of trenches were dug over many decades.

Left: A Blaw-Knox BK50 truck-mounted dragshovel hard at work for the Royal Engineers regiment of the British Army. This model saw service around the world from the late 1950s and on into the 1960s.

Right: Hard rock will prove no trouble to this powerful Northwest 6 dragshovel at work during the 1960s or 1970s.

SKIMMERS

Although extremely popular among public works contractors and with small clay pit operators, the skimmer became obsolete with the introduction of other forms of excavation equipment, not least the crawler-mounted tractor shovels, by the end of the 1950s.

It was an ideal machine for lifting and loading old tarmac and materials which did not require deep digging. As its name implies, it merely skimmed its bucket out along the boom until it was full and ready to be hoisted clear of the ground by raising the boom.

Above: **This is a Priestman excavator fitted with skimmer at work for the Army's Royal Engineers regiment in Burma 1944.**

Above left: **A Ransomes & Rapier 4.5–0 skimmer.**

Left: **A Ransomes & Rapier model 410 universal excavator, fitted here with a skimmer of ⅜cu yd capacity. The skimmer bucket on this machine is also designed for use as a face shovel, backacter and a skimmer, while, with the addition of an insert fitted into the end of the boom, it can also be used as a 2 ton-capacity crane. It was built in the 1940s and designed to compete with the Ruston-Bucyrus 10 R–B, the Priestman Cub, the Smith Super 8 & 10, and the Blaw-Knox BK50 from British manufacturers.**

The bucket emptied by releasing a latch whereby the bucket floor swung open to release the excavated material.

In all, the skimmer was an important part of the excavating industry's inventory for many decades, stretching from the earliest examples during the late 1800s until it disappeared during the early 1960s, by which time the track type tractor shovels were doing much of the work once assigned to the skimmer. It was ideal for assisting in the removal of old road surfaces, stripping top soil, removing shallow overburden seams above clay and coal deposits, and even loading coal and other minerals from seams in opencast mining. It was able to load earth from stockpiles but without the same facility as the face shovel.

One Ransomes & Rapier 414 excavator was certainly used to strip overburden from china clay deposits on Dartmoor during the 1950s before giving way to a much smaller 10 R–B face shovel.

GRAB CRANES AND OTHER FRONT-END EQUIPMENT

The universal excavator was adaptable as face shovel, dragshovel, skimmer, dragline, grabbing crane, crane, pile-driver, auger, boom and log-loader.

Priestman's of Hull, who were generally well known for their large range of grab buckets to fit just about any type of crane, also produced a side dragline which, having the benefit of a pole and sheave attached, was able to excavate ditches at 180°.

Here are some of the uses to which excavators can be put using crane type jibs or booms.

Above left: A Priestman steam-powered grabbing crane from the 1920s, fitted with a specially adapted gun-carriage type carrier which was operated from off the machine with controls located on the track frames.

Left: Priestman grab type crane (steam-powered) fitted with a unique tank-type undercarriage, almost certainly *c*1920s.

Above right: Although difficult to identify, this rail-mounted grab crane at work in a Cornish china clay pit is thought to be a Ruston, though the model is unknown. It would have been in operation during the 1920s and 1930s.

Right: A Priestman barge-mounted grab crane, powered by steam, working on the middle level of the Welland & Deeping Canal *c*1940.

Left: A Ransomes & Rapier steam-powered, barge-mounted grab crane cleaning the levels for the Welland & Deeping Canal Commissioners in 1940.

Below left: A Weserhutte type W800 crawler-mounted grab crane from Germany making short work of loading wooden rail trucks in the 1940s.

Above: A Russian E–100N grab crane excavator from the mid-1960s.

Above right: A Weserhutte W80 excavator from the mid-1960s is the ideal machine with which to demolish a tall building, using its excavating grab, which can then be used to load the debris into trucks.

Right: An Osgood excavator working near the Rhine in Germany for the Royal Engineers regiment of the British Army in 1945 on pile driving duties. Osgood machines were made from the 1880s through to the mid-1950s when they were acquired by the Marion Power Shovel Co and ceased production.

Above: A Link-Belt Speeder excavator model LS–418 using an almighty auger during the early 1970s on a USA project.

Right: This large Weserhutte excavator, likely to be a model W180 or similar, has no difficulty in handling a very long piling rig in the 1970s.

STRIPPING SHOVELS

These machines were designed primarily to remove the deep overburden above coal seams, iron-ore deposits and phosphates, though they were occasionally engaged to extract deep layers of clay for the production of bricks or materials used in the production of cement. The two pioneers who conceived the idea of a long range stripping shovel first approached the Marion Steam Shovel Co, which was not in any way taken with the idea at first, though in 1911 it was the Marion Co which produced a model 250 steam-powered stripping shovel. The following year the Bucyrus Company produced its first stripping shovel and throughout the era of stripping shovel manufacture incorporated all the latest features. Both these major USA manufacturers competed vigorously for their share of the market, each pioneering new develop-

ments, such as the 'knee action front end' from Marion, which was designed to further crowd the bucket into the deep overburden banks without overloading the long booms with heavy additional equipment. There was also the development of four-corner, self-levelling travelling gear — initially these machines were rail-mounted — until the introduction of four sets of dual crawlers became the norm.

For one company to poach engineers from another was frowned upon, and even one stripping shovel engineer sitting on the same train as another from the rival company was looked upon as industrial espionage of the highest order. The competition

Below: **A Wilson steam-powered stripping shovel made around 1900 and used at Preston's Pit at Weldon in the Midlands ironstone mines for Lloyd's.**

Left: **A steam-powered stripping shovel, believed to be a Ruston & Hornsby model 300 from the early 1920s, in the ironstone quarries of the Midlands.**

The steam-powered stripping shovel started work in 1908. The much larger electrically-powered Ransomes & Rapier 5360 took over as heavyweight excavator in the brickworks of Bedfordshire from the late 1920s until walking draglines came in after World War 2.

Marion introduced the 5560-M, an 18cu yd stripping shovel in 1832, while Bucyrus-Erie had introduced a model 750-B, followed by the 950-B during the 1930s and the 1050B in the very early 1940s. All were to feature a counterbalance hoist system to help increase the digging cycle.

Although capacities had increased to the 30cu yd region with the larger models, the 1950s brought with them the biggest advances in stripping shovel size and technology, with Marion's 60cu yd 5760 being introduced in 1956. This was by all standards a truly mammoth shovel. 'The Mountaineer' was the first of five, all of which went to work at North American strip coal mines, followed by the even larger Marion 5761 of 70cu yd-plus capacity. These were joined by shovels of equal proportions from Bucyrus-Erie such as the 1650-B, 1850-B, 1950-B and by the 3850-B introduced in 1962, by which

between the two suppliers in the USA was intense but competition from any other shovel manufacturer did not exist.

Over in Britain, however, companies were manufacturing stripping shovels for use in the brick clay industry and for work in the ironstone mines of the Midlands. Ruston and Hornsby, and Ransomes & Rapier of Ipswich were by far the leading contributors, though Whitaker of Leeds and Wilson's of Liverpool certainly produced one each, and A. R. Grossmith joined a few of the Bucyrus-made stripping shovels which crossed the Atlantic to work in the ironstone mines.

The Ransomes & Rapier model 5360 was based on the Marion-designed 360 which made its début in 1923 in the USA. As a consequence, the R & R 5360 outsold all other such machines, with 13 being produced over an eight year period from 1934.

The London Brick Co personnel had been to see a long boom steam crane navvy at work for S. J. Lloyd at the Corby Ironworks, where it had been in operation since 1895. Percy Malcolm Stewart (who was the Managing Director of the brickmakers B. J. Forder & Son) approached Lloyd to ask if his engineer A. R. Grossmith would build a similar machine for use at Forder's Stewartby clay pit.

Right: **A Bucyrus 320-B steam stripping shovel from 1923 working at an iron-ore range in the USA. The machine was built at the South Milwaukee plant in Wisconsin.**

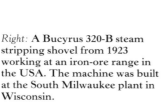

time the 100cu yd dippers had already become familiar. Then in 1965 came an enormous 180cu yd-capacity for the biggest shovel ever built... the Marion 6360-M. Known as 'The Captain', its specifications were as follows:

Dipper capacity – 180cu yd

Boom length – 215ft from centre of foot pins to centre of boom point sheaves.

Dipper handle – 133ft

Crowd handle – 102ft

Stiff leg (knee action) – 104ft

Boom point sheave diameter – 144in

Boom padlock sheave pitch diameter – 120in

Hoist cable 3.5in in diameter (of which there were four on a double hitch).

Boom support cables (8 bridge strand) 3.6 in

With a total horsepower of 33,000, each of its eight tracks were 16ft high and 44ft in length. It worked at the Captain Mine near Percy, Illinois, USA, from 1965 until it was destroyed by fire in September 1991.

Of the two huge Bucyrus-Erie 3850-Bs that were made, the first, in 1962, went to the Sinclair Mine in Kentucky for Peabody Coal and had a 115cu yd bucket, while in August 1964 'The River King', went to work at the River King Mine near Marissa,

Above: **The Ransomes & Rapier 5360 stripping shovel working here at Glendon Bridge is one of 13 similar machines to have worked at the Midlands iron-ore quarries, all built between 1934 and 1942. Others were sold to the London Brick Co clay pits in Bedfordshire.**

Illinois, again for Peabody Coal. This time it carried a 140 cu yd dipper and was in continual use until it was retired in August 1992. During its 28 years of operation it had dug its way some 20 miles from one end of the mine to the site of its final dig. Sadly it is no more, as this and all but one or two of these fine shovels by either of the manufacturers have been cut up for scrap — and that is one big heap of scrap when you consider that one of the 3850–Bs weighed in at 8,800 tons and the 6360 Marion at 12,631 tons. At least two stripping shovels have now been preserved in museum type situations in Canada and in the USA. One, a 950–B from 1932, is well cared for by an enthusiastic band of volunteers near Alberta in Canada, and the other, 'The Silver Spade', one of the two huge Bucyrus-Erie 1950-Bs (the other was known as 'The Gem of Egypt') will be preserved for inspection by the interested public when it ends its career in 1995.

'The Gem of Egypt' had a capacity of 130cu yd with each bite, while 'The Silver Spade' was equipped with a 105cu yd dipper; both machines were over 7,000 tons in weight and were over 200ft tall and as wide as an 8-lane highway.

Right: The Marion 5761 at the Lynnville Mine, another operated by the Peabody Coal Company, was further evidence of yet larger shovels to come. This one was already in the 70cu yd-capacity class.

Below right: A close-up of 5761 Marion stripping shovel clearly showing its knee action crowd and sets of dual crawlers on which the huge shovel travels. They might look somewhat similar to the two huge crawler units which carry the rockets to the launch area at Cape Canaveral — and they should do, as those were built by Marion using stripping shovel technology and experience, the main difference being that these huge shovels are electrically powered whereas the crawler transporters are diesel driven.

Above: The Lima 1201 shovel was normally fitted with conventional front-end shovel equipment. In this case, however, a long range boom and dipper handle were used to haul a 3.5cu yd bucket through the overburden on this opencast coal site near Newcastle in Northeast England in 1944.

Right: The era of the super shovel had arrived. Gigantic shovels such as this, the Marion 5760, dwarfed all they surveyed, as is depicted in this painting by Ron McKee. 'The Mountaineer' started work at a surface coal mine near Cadiz, Ohio, in 1956, making it possible to uncover coal deposits which would have been too expensive or impossible to mine using any other method (though in certain formations bucket-wheel excavators have been employed).

Above: **The Marion model 5323 stripping shovel was the smallest of the specialist stripping shovel range. Of the nine machines made, one came to work in Scunthorpe for UK Ironstone in the British steel industry. It started work in 1961 and was shipped to India to work in a surface coal mine after UK Ironstone closed down in the early 1970s. This was without doubt the largest shovel ever to work in Western Europe. One other 5323 stripping shovel was shipped to Brazil in 1954. The large stripping shovel business was mostly restricted to the USA, for the two leading manufacturers were American, though such machines were produced in the former Soviet Union for work mainly in internal coal mines.**

Centre right: **The Marion 5900 stripping shovel was the last of this type of excavator to have been made by Marion or indeed its competitor Bucyrus-Erie. All future orders were to be for walking draglines and ever larger electric mining shovels with matching 240-plus capacity haul-trucks. The 5900 was a 105cu yd-capacity stripping shovel which went to work at a mine in Illinois in 1971. These photographs show some of the major parts of this monster machine before it was assembled out on the site. The size of the hoist drum can be gauged by the engineers working on it at the factory in Marion, Ohio.**

Right: **The crawler side frame (one of the eight) used on the Marion 5900 stripping shovel, still being machined at the Marion factory.**

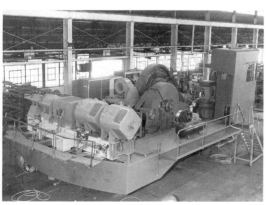

Above: **The Marion 291–M was claimed to be the largest shovel in the world to be fitted with conventional two crawlers. This machine was especially designed as a long-reach parting shovel to remove overburden between one coal seam and another or for removing overburden at relatively shallow depths. Working for Peabody Coal Co, it is equipped with a 15cu yd dipper on a 90ft boom.**

Left: The Marion 191-M electric mining shovel, machinery deck and operator's cab, during assembly at the Marion factory, prior to shipment to the customer's site, where final assembly of the tracks, machinery housing, boom, dipper handle and dipper would take place.

Right: This photograph shows one of the first mobile truck-mounted cranes by the subsidiary of Thew-Lorain, the international crane manufacturing and rental company, of Lorain, Ohio, in the 1920s.

Centre right: This photograph shows the largest shovel bucket of all, from the Marion 6360 stripping shovel. It has a 180cu yd capacity and the two men who can be seen standing beside it give some idea of just how big it was.

Below: The Marion 6360 stripping shovel at 12,631 tons is by far the biggest shovel ever built, despite the fact that even larger shovels were designed, not least by Marion's only competitor Bucyrus-Erie. None got further than the drawing board as the era of the 'Super Shovel' had gone, only to be replaced by super draglines and bucket-wheel systems. The thought of shovels larger than the 6360 leaves one to ponder, how big is big? With all of these enormous excavators, surely it is physically possible to transform not just the area contained in a surface mine, but whole mountain ranges and indeed countries.

WALKING DRAGLINES

These unique machines were first developed from an idea of John W. Page, who was a partner in a company building the Henepin Canal, near Colona, Illinois, USA, in 1904.

A machine which could stand clear of the excavation, yet still operate its bucket to remove the soil, rock and clays, was the perfect answer to a canal engineer's (and, later, mining companies') dreams.

Although initially such machines were limited in their mobility, being generally propped up on heavy timbers and moved by means of steel rollers, many did eventually progress to operating from rail lines. As with the early shovels, they were fitted with self-laying crawler tracks, but it was the walking device developed by Oscar J. Martinson which, when fitted to the early Monaghan machines (jointly produced by Page and Monaghan), set the walking dragline on its

path to becoming the most widely accepted mining excavator. It is as popular in the 1990s as it has been through the many decades since its inception in 1913.

In the vast surface mines, where overburden to great depths has to be removed to uncover coal, phosphates, diamonds, ironstone and occasionally limestone, walking draglines with bucket capacities from around 2.5cu yd to the massive 220cu yd, 13,000-ton 'Big Muskie' are never far away.

Page (now P & H), the Marion Company of Ohio, and Bucyrus-Erie, also of the USA, along with Ruston Bucyrus (now Bucyrus Europe) and Ransomes & Rapier of Ipswich, Suffolk, England (now under the

Below: **A Ransomes & Rapier model W-150 at Stewartby, Bedfordshire, stripping brick clay for the London Brick Co.**

Above: **With a capacity of 6 tons of clay/bucket load, this W-150 is loading an electric hopper feed, taking the clay to the kilns outside the pit area in the 1950s and 1960s.**

Below: **The Ruston-Bucyrus 5-W was one of the most popular draglines on opencast mine sites throughout Britain from the Lincoln-based excavator makers. This particular machine was employed throughout the 1950s and 1960s by the United Steel Co division at their ironstone operation in Scunthorpe. A similar machine was once a familiar sight parked on the side of the road in a village in the Welsh coal-mining valleys during the early 1960s. It was evidently awaiting a new location or perhaps (sadly) the scrapmen. It appears that the local children found it one of the most unusual play things anyone could wish for — most of us had to make do with an old car or a lorry, but a walking dragline? It was almost certainly one of the 50 or so 5-Ws made by Ruston-Bucyrus between 1939 and the 1970s.**

management of Bucyrus Europe), were responsible for almost the entire output of walking draglines outside of the former Soviet countries, where many manufacturing plants supply a wide variety of walking draglines of all sizes up to the 10,000-ton-plus class. Many Russian-made draglines have been sold to surface mines outside Russia — to India, the Middle East, Cuba and elsewhere — while American and British-made machines are hard at work from the harsh climate of northern Canada to the huge coalfields in the outback of Australia, from opencast coal sites in England, Scotland and Wales and to South Africa, the phosphate regions of Jordan and Morocco, and not least throughout the USA, in coal and phosphates, chiefly in Florida.

Basically a walking dragline sits on a large-diameter, round base (or tub, as it is known) when digging. The main superstructure revolves on its roller path from dig to dump point or when obtaining the direction in which it might be required to move, which in all cases is backwards,

away from the boom and bucket. When moving, two huge shoes are brought into contact with the ground by means of a cam system which carries the legs. On the largest American and Russian machines this function is operated by a hydraulically controlled set of rams, for both lifting the machine and for moving it horizontally. On all other machines the walking mechanism is controlled by specially designed gearing driven by the dragline's electric motors or diesel power units. The whole machine is lifted and slid along the ground until it is again lowered on to its base, prior to returning the shoes to the floor when a second step is required. Because of the low ground pressure exerted by the machine's large tub and shoes, it is an ideal machine for working in places where crawler machines would find the going difficult. The vast majority of walking draglines are electrically powered, with just a very few at the lower end of the range which are available

with diesel engines, though for this reason they are normally purchased for use on one site for a number of years, after which they have to be totally stripped down and rebuilt on relocation at other sites.

Many large draglines have been known to work for 40 or more years on one site before being moved to mines elsewhere in their own country or indeed abroad.

Right: **This is one of the three Ransomes & Rapier W1400s ordered by the steel companies beginning with the first order in 1947 and two more in the mid-1950s. This one is at the Priors Hall site near Corby. All three operations are clearly visible in this photograph: overburden stripping by the W1400, drilling for blasting using the Ruston-Bucyrus (probably 100 R-B) former shovel as a drilling platform, the Appleyard type drills on the ironstone seam and there are loading operations in the foreground.**

Below: **The Ransomes & Rapier W-600 made in 1952 for the United Steel Co shows its superior size against the little W-90 also from R & R, both at the huge Scunthorpe complex. Note the two Caterpillar D8s and the Ruston-Bucyrus 110 R-B face shovel.**

However, there have been one or two exceptions. One walking dragline was moved a distance of seven miles from one site to another across country under its own power as early as the 1940s.

One of the large Rapier draglines operating in the Midlands ironstone industry was required to walk a distance of 13 miles (is this a world record?) and 'Big Geordie', a Bucyrus Erie 1550–W, then the largest excavator in Western Europe (now superseded by a P & H 757, 'The Ace of Spades'), was required to walk over 2.5 miles from the Sisters opencast coal site to Butterwell OCCS in Northumberland during the early 1970s, crossing three roads, a railway line and a river on its journey. Three thousand six hundred tons of excavator walking the fields of Northumberland must have been a sight that the locals will long remember.

The photographs in this chapter are designed to show a cross-section of some of the more familiar walking draglines in use over the past 50 or so years. Many are seen at work in Britain, North America, Australia and in Russia.

Left: **One of the two W-1800s to work at the Midlands iron-ore quarries. The 1400s were equipped with 20–22cu yd buckets whereas the W-1800s had 33cu yd buckets. The W-1800s are somewhat similar to the one delivered to the large anthracite opencast mine in Glynneath, South Wales, where it operated a 40cu yd bucket from a 247ft boom, in 1961. Bought initially for £900,000 it worked day and night until it was stripped and after the second refurbishment had been completed during its long career it was sold to a mining company in the USA for considerably more than its original price, a fitting testimony to this super dragline. It was the largest excavator in Western Europe until 'Big Geordie' (a Bucyrus-Erie 1550-W) took the title in August 1969 when it started work on another opencast coal site, this time in the northeast of England.**

Below left: **The size of the W-1800s at Corby can be judged by the Euclid C-6 bulldozer nearby and the men standing close to its huge walking shoes. This particular machine is at Great Oakley.**

Above right: **A Marion 7400–M walking dragline on the move at this Scunthorpe iron-ore mine.**

Centre right: **This Marion 7400–M slipped into the cut at Logdyke Lane opencast coal site in 1957. The task of recovering a huge walking dragline from such a mishap must have proved to be a very big job indeed. With almost a hundred Marion 7400s in service around the world from 1940 there is little doubt that it was among Marion's most popular walking draglines.**

Right: **This Russian-made EW 10/60 walking dragline is one of hundreds made at a number of factories in the mining regions of Russia. The sheer size of this machine can be seen by the men in the vicinity of the walking shoes.**

Other Russian draglines have operating weights well in excess of 10,000 tons.

Left: In March 1970, the National Coal Board Opencast Executive awarded a £5 million contract to Wimpey to win 1,600,000 tons of coal at Mabel Plantation in Cumberland over a period of seven years. A Marion 7500–M walking dragline was the main item of stripping equipment on the site, along with the Lima 2400 crawler dragline and the much smaller 22 R-B shovels for clean up and coal loading.

Right: From 1949, four Bucyrus-Erie 1150B walking draglines were imported from the USA to help win valuable opencast coal following the war years when demand from electricity suppliers and domestic users along with the railways and industry was at a premium. Almost all of these machines had already been at work in the mines in North America and at least one was employed along the banks of the massive Mississippi, building levees in an effort to control the severe flooding frequently, and still, experienced. Many draglines have been employed in these efforts including a large Marion diesel-powered crawler dragline, the model 184.

This is one of the 1150Bs at a British opencast coal site. It may well be the last of the four to survive.

Below: This is the 45cu yd-capacity Marion 7820–M walking dragline which was introduced in 1970 to join the other four models in the Marion 7000 series of walking draglines.

Above: **The Bucyrus-Erie 1370–W** was available with bucket capacities of 60cu yd. These large draglines were sold to coal mines in New Mexico and Indiana, USA, and the Florida phosphate mines, while further 1370s went to work in New South Wales, Australia.

Left: **Once again Peabody Coal Co** were also the purchasers of another large walking dragline, this time the Bucyrus-Erie 2560–W, which in common with many of Peabody's massive machines is up in the 100cu yd-capacity range. Peabody Coal were among the world's top five users of a vast inventory of very large stripping shovels, walking draglines, coal loaders and bucket-wheel excavators.

Above: **The Marion 8000 series of walking draglines represents a whole range of walking draglines of which there are well in excess of 100 very large machines at work in mines in South Africa, the USA, Canada and Australia, each moving millions of cubic yards of overburden each year to reach the coal, lignite and other minerals. Among them are the model 8400–M, one of which went to work in Morocco in 1969, equipped with a 63cu yd bucket to strip for phosphates.**

Centre left: **To achieve the maximum results from both the machines and operators, the three leading manufacturers of walking draglines in the USA run on–site operators' courses to ensure those huge buckets are returned full of earth, rock and dirt and to see it is placed on the dumps in such a manner as to ensure the safety of tips and the minimum of bulldozing to level them out afterwards. In this photograph an operator undergoes tuition from a Marion instructor on the 8400–M walking dragline.**

Below left: **These are the huge swing gear cases for a Marion 8400 walking dragline in the fitting shop before assembly on the dragline. The large components will be fitted in the field as part of its site assembly programme.**

Left: A joint mining venture at the Warkworth mine in Australia between Costain Mining and the Australian owner of the mine to win millions of tons of coal for export to Japan and Europe called for a large walking dragline, in this case a Bucyrus-Erie 1370–W which, with its 63cu yd bucket is similar to two machines working at Costain's Ravensworth Mine during the early 1970s. With coal reserves estimated to last many decades it is likely that these machines will have many years of work at these two mines. This view of Warkworth shows the stripping operations with the big dragline and the coal seam.

Right: One of Marion's best-selling top-of-the-range draglines is currently the model 8750–M, which was first introduced in 1983, with machines now at work in Canada, the USA and in Australia, with booms of 420ft and buckets of over 100cu yd-capacity. On at least one large surface mine in Australia two 8750s are stripping overburden to reach the shallow coal deposits. The Marion 8750 in this photograph is one of the many large excavators used by Peabody Coal.

Above: **The Marion 8950–M** walking dragline which worked at the Amax Coal Ayrshire mine, near Chandler, Indiana, was the only 8950 to be made. Here the huge 150cu yd bucket is being made. The machine started work in 1973.

Left: One of only two Marion 8900s made in 1966–67. One went to work in Indiana, USA, and the other to the Moura Mine in Australia. Equipped with 145cu yd buckets it was certainly one of the largest excavators ever to appear on the Australian continent.

Right: Spec sheet of Marion 8900, 'The Big Digger at Dugger'.

"THE BIG DIGGER AT DUGGER"

Marion 8900 Dragline
DUGGER MINE
PEABODY COAL COMPANY

* Weighs 14,000,000 pounds

* "A" frame equals height of 14-story building

* Required nearly one year and 55,000 manhours to erect at nearby location -- 115 railroad cars hauled prefabricated parts to erection site

* Boom is 250 feet long - height from tip of boom to coal seam nearly equals height of Statue of Liberty

* Housing is as large as many of the smaller gymnasiums

* Moves itself by walking

* Cables are 4 inches diameter

* 145 cubic yard bucket, weighs 100 tons empty, stands 3 stories tall — picks up 430,000 pounds of dirt and rock with each scoop

* Thirty electric motors develops 18,000 horsepower

* Consumes enough electricity to supply a city of 20,000-25,000 people

* Three men -- operator, oiler, groundman -- operate this machine. Operator sits in an air-conditioned cab 38 feet above ground level

THIS MACHINE OPERATES AROUND-THE-CLOCK, SHUTS DOWN ONLY FOR MAINTENANCE

Right: Spec sheet of 'Big Geordie' Bucyrus-Erie 1550–W.

Below: The size of some of these huge buckets can be gauged by the size of the people standing nearby or, as with the 65cu yd bucket from 'Big Geordie', the B–E 1550–W, two large cars side by side within its bucket.

Right: The largest walking dragline in the world is this Bucyrus-Erie 4250W. With a bucket capacity of 220cu yd (or just short of 300 tons) and 45,000hp and with a weight of 12,244 tons, it is one of the largest mobile land machines in existence. This photograph of its front, taken while it was still being erected on site in Ohio, USA, gives some idea of its enormity as compared with the man standing on the top of the fairlead, near the operator's cabin. A second man stands near the machine's roller circle at the bottom of the fairlead.

BUCYRUS ERIE 1550-W WALKING DRAGLINE
Walking Traction Mounting   Electrically Driven
(Independent Motor Walking)
MAIN SPECIFICATIONS

Length of boom	265'
Working weight, approx. (with bucket),lbs.	6,400,000
Walking Traction Mounting.	**55' Base**
Width & length of shoes.	10' x 56'
Bearing area of both sides,sq.ft.	1120
Diameter of cam.	8'-0"
Length of step (approx.)	8'-6"
Overall width over shoes.	77'-8"
Approx.walking speed,mph.	0.16
Base.	**55'Dia.**
Outside diameter.	55'-0"
Bearing area, sq.ft.	2375
Diameter of rail circle.	46'-0"
Number of rollers.	120
Average diameter of rollers.	12"
Pitch diameter of swing rack.	38'-4"
Revolving Frame	
Width x length, upper machinery frame, approximate.	44' x 90'
Depth of girders, upper machinery frame, feet.	11
Hoist rope sheaves, boom point, P.D.	120"

Electrical Equipment

Hoist motors (blown)	4	625 hp @ 230 V) / 1250 hp @ 460 V)
Drag motors (blown)	4	625 hp @ 230 V) / 1250 hp @ 460 V)
Swing motors (blown)	4	300 hp @ 230 V) / 600 hp @ 460 V)
Walking motors	4	187-1/2 hp @ 230 V) / 375 hp @ 460 V)

The above motors are rated at 75°C. Cont.
Generators for Ward-Leonard drive are equivalent in capacity to their respective motors, and are driven by suitable motors.

Boom Length	Operating Radius (B)	Boom Angle	Max. Suspended Load (Lbs.)	Height Boom Pt.Pin (I)	Depth of Dig. (H)	Drag Drum Dia.	Drag Rope No.	Drag Rope Dia.	Hoist Drum Dia.	Hoist Rope No.	Hoist Rope Dia.
265'	233'	40°	341,000	186'	150'	92"	2	3¼"	92"	2	3⅛"

76

Hydraulic Excavators

The use of hydraulics is not new on excavating equipment or indeed in excavation generally.

Many minerals, including china clay, gold and tin, have been washed out of the surrounding rock for many generations, using high-pressure water hoses.

In the operation of machinery, using oil under pressure to force a piston out of its sleeve was first experimented with by Sir W. G. Armstrong, whose variations began during the 1880s, and certainly an excavating machine using hydraulics was used to build the Alexandra Dock in Hull on Humberside.

Other experimental hydraulic excavators appeared at various stages from the early years of the 20th century, although it was after World War 2 that mass introduction of hydraulic excavators took place and by the end of the 1960s they replaced many of the cable type excavators that had dominated the industry for so many decades. By the 1990s, the hydraulic excavator (including the front shovel, backacter and digger/loader mounted on tracks or wheels) became as common a sight on our high streets as the city bus. In large-scale quarrying, civil engineering and in surface mining, operators can now choose between the large electric mining shovels, bucket-wheel systems, draglines or very large hydraulic excavators. With machines of weights approaching 1,000 tons, the hydraulic excavators are certainly becoming acceptable. In copper, iron ore, phosphates and in coal mining, these very sleek, high-tech, computer-aided machines are certainly making great inroads.

Above: **This truck-mounted hydraulic excavator, the Poclain Model TL from 1952, is one of this company's earliest excavators. It paved the way for a vast range which by the 1960s included the giant EC1000.**

Over recent years, the development in the use of hydraulic motors is seemingly endless, from the very small to the very large. Hydraulic motors have been adapted to operate bucket-wheel excavators and the travel-mode of the large cable draglines, and we have fully hydraulic cable-operated cranes and draglines. The 'old' mechanical drives to the winding drums have been replaced by hydraulic motors. Another recent development has been the long-reach hydraulic excavator which is now able to clean lakes, ponds and waterways or reach down embankments to depths which would once have been practical only with the cable dragline. The VC range of long-reach excavators, developed initially by Priestman's of Hull, is now being produced by RBI, the newly formed Ruston-Bucyrus International, of

Lincoln, whose original company first manufactured steam shovels as early as 1875. Koehring's of North America led the way with extra-long booms and dipper sticks on their hydraulic excavators for many years. Their 466, 666, 505 and 1066 models, for instance, were demonstrated against similar sized cable draglines with notable success. The speed at which the hydraulic excavator could lower its bucket, fill, return and s1ew to dump was far greater than that of the cable machines. As early as 1971, when a book was written by Koehrings to show the comparison charts, the day of the hydraulic excavator had already began to push aside the cable dragline, certainly in the contractor-size 1¼ to 3cu yd-capacity class at least.

Above: Off the truck and under its own power this wheel-mounted Poclain Model TP from 1956 was yet another progression — a front shovel version.

Left: For many years the name Dinkum-Digger was synonymous with Whitlocks' range of wheel-mounted tractor digger/loaders, followed by full slew hydraulic excavators and Dinkum-Dumpers. Here we see one of the early digger/loaders from the beginning of the 1950s working on a site in South Devon.

Above right: The one machine which just about everyone has heard of and seen is the JCB from Joseph Cyril Bamford. So much so that almost every digger/loader is christened the 'JCB' whether made by that company or not. It was first built in the very early 1950s and, like the early Dinkum-Digger, based around a Fordson tractor, though eventually all but the engines were made by JCB. One of the most popular models of the 1950s and early 1960s would have been the JCB4. The particular one shown here is on a road widening contract in the Torbay area of South Devon.

Right: The JCB3C took over in popularity among customers of the JCB hydraulic excavator for many years. British designed, it is built and sold in vast numbers around the world. Without doubt JCB are one of the industry's leading manufacturers of hydraulic excavators of the wheel digger/loader type, coupled with their range of fully slewing tracked excavators from the range of mini-diggers up to the 7 to 43-ton class made jointly with Sumitomo of Japan.

Right: **The JCB3C was the forerunner of the JCB3CX, which was amongst the first of its kind to feature an almost total-vision cab, with much more toughened glass than on previous machines.**

Above: **By the riverside or on the high street you don't have to go far to see a JCB at work. There are more manufacturers of digger/loaders and tracked or wheel fully slewing excavators than ever before, ranging from successful family-run concerns to multinational companies. Some have been in the excavator/earthmoving equipment manufacturing business for many decades, while others had never previously made an excavating machine of any type prior to producing the latest high-tech models now available. With such refinements as 'bend in the middle' dippersticks and booms, for example, an excavator is now able to locate the bucket to the left or right without moving the main boom in any direction. Extending dipper sticks have been available for some years, but the versatility is now endless.**

Left: **The JCB807 is one of JCB's earlier models of tracked, fully slew excavators.**

Above: **A JCB805B** cleaning coal on this British opencast coal site, the Ryefield OCC site in the north of England.

Centre left: This little wheel-mounted Atlas excavator is at work for a river board in the West Country during the early 1960s. Many of the very latest mobile excavators have hopped off the tracks and back on to road tyres. This will give them the freedom to travel from job to job along the road without having to use low loader transporters. They will also be able to work on tarmac without scarring the roads in the way crawler tracks do. Nevertheless, these tyres are an *extension* of choice, as track laying excavators are still very much with us, from the little 0.5-ton rubber or steel-tracked mini models up through the ranks to those huge mining-size machines.

Below left: This Atlas model AB1702 was made by the German company founded in 1919. They first produced excavators in the very late 1940s and improved on their early hydraulic grab-type range by adding truck-mounted and self-propelled wheeled and tracked excavators throughout the second half of the 1950s.

Above: **The front shovel model AB2002 from Atlas was at home in quarries around the Continent and in Britain for many years. Current Atlas excavators range from 8-wheeled and 10-tracked models from the 404 to the 2004, 20 to 2000 litres capacity.**

Centre right: A more unusual type of hydraulic excavator is this telescopic boom type from Warner-Swasey, manufacturers of the Gradall. This photograph shows one of the first Gradalls mounted on a track-drive Linn truck in the early 1940s. Similar telescopic boom type machines were also made by the Quickway Crane and Excavator Co of Denver, Colorado, USA. This company was acquired by the Marion Power Shovel Co in the late 1950s. Some machines of this type were operated by cables rather than hydraulics. Others manufactured included Badger and Bantam by Koehring.

Below right: This truck-mounted Hydro Scoop by Warner-Swasey is the model 300. Its twisting wrist action made it a very versatile excavator and grader all in one.

Above: **This tracked Gradall model G–660 is one of a range of telescopic boom excavators from Warner-Swasey produced during the 1960s.**

Right: **A more traditional hydraulic excavator from Warner-Swasey of the USA is this top-of-the-range model 1900, ably assisted by a Cat D8 bulldozer. The Hopto 1900 was one of the few made in the 100-ton range during the 1960s and 1970s.**

Right: Traditional is not a word which could be used to describe this French excavator, which looked normal enough when travelling, but when working it sat on a base and revolved, thus turning itself into a fully slewing excavator. Made by Pingon Smaliev, this type of excavator was widely demonstrated throughout Britain. In this photograph it reflects closely the concepts of the skid-steer machines, now widely used on small wheel loaders.

Below: This photograph of the Pingon Sitting Bull demonstrates its work ability.

Left: This is a model 3980 hydraulic excavator from the International Harvester Co of the USA, and indeed worldwide, later acquired and marketed under the Dresser Industries name. This was the track type model.

Below left: First of the International Harvester wheeled excavators to be sold in Britain was this model 3945, bought by Macdonald Brothers & Co of Portree, Isle of Skye, from the dealer James Bowen & Sons Ltd. It was one of a range of 5-wheeled and tracked excavators introduced by International Harvester during the 1960s.

It is being used for the extraction of gravel on the company's shore-based quarry. Its road speed of 12mph enabled it to work at other locations for the company on general excavating and loading duties. Whereas tracked machines were popular with contractors in Britain, wheeled versions were popular on the Continent, and it seems we too have now gone totally European in this respect.

Below: One of the original manufacturers of cable type excavators was NCK-Rapier. Their models were made under licensing agreements with the American Koehring. Here a 466 is loading an Aveling Barford haul-truck.

Above: **This NCK-Rapier model 475 is loading coal straight from the seam at this opencast coal site in Scotland in 1973.**

Right: **A side view of the NCK-Rapier 475 hydraulic backacter excavator from the early 1970s.**

Below right: **This model 1066 hydraulic backhoe from NCK–Rapier is identical to the Koehring 1066 made by the same company in the USA.**

Above: The P & H company of North America were manufacturers, under licence, of the O & K range of hydraulic excavators of Germany. This photograph features the RH25 on demonstration at Cobb Rock Quarry, near Beaverton, Oregon, in December 1971.

Right: This is a P & H model 72–69A hydraulic backacter excavator from the late 1960s or early 1970s.

Below: This is a P & H model 72–70A hydraulic excavator in the early 1970s.

Right: A model 73–50G P & H hydraulic excavator from the 1970s.

Below right: In much the same way as all digger/loaders were labelled 'JCB', the 'Hy–Mac' label was applied to hydraulic excavators throughout the 1960s, irrespective of their manufacture. This model 480 was the first to be produced at the South Wales factory of the Rhymney Engineering Company in 1962. Models that followed included the 580 and the largest, the 1080. The Hy–Mac was the first British hydraulic excavator of the track type to be produced in a British factory. In this photograph the 480 is clearing brushwood at Cummery Corner on the A30 in Devon in advance of a road widening scheme.

Below: The Hy–Mac 580 and larger 1080 are both working on a trenching contract in Devon in the early 1970s.

Above right: The Hy–Mac 580 fitted with a ripper tooth shows its versatility.

Right: The Poclain TY45 was a revolutionary excavator with its unique triangular base and its steering wheels situated at the apex of the triangle. It was without doubt a very versatile excavator, being able to climb with relative ease using its own powerful hydraulics.

Above: **This tracked excavator is the Poclain model TCS seen here with a long dipper arm and extra long and wide tracks for work in soft ground conditions.**

Above left: **The Poclain FY30, like all of the Continental wheel-mounted excavators, was very popular due to its mobility both on and off the site.**

Left: **An LY8O Poclain hydraulic excavator is featured here using an hydraulic clamshell (grab) during the late 1960s/early 1970s. At demonstrations run by one dealer in the West Country a popular party trick was to rotate a TY45 with a heavy-duty grab bucket until it achieved speed, then count the revolutions per minute, which with the aid of the centrifugal force could attain 19.5rpm!**

Right: **One of the smaller Poclain models was this little FC30.**

Above: **The TYS as a wheel version differs from the TY as it has returned to the more conventional 4-wheel undercarriage.**

Below: **This Poclain model TX is operating an hydraulic grab between the trench sheets on this sewer project. Extra long arms were available to which the grabs could be attached enabling them to reach abnormal depths.**

Right: **This LC80 Poclain is using a V–ditching bucket on this contract during the early 1970s.**

Above left: **A Poclain SC150** being used to lower concrete pipes ever so carefully into a trench it has dug, photographed around 1971.

Left: **This LC80** with front shovel equipment is working in a Devon ball clay works. Another LC80 with extra long and wide tracks, equipped with a long boom and dipper arm, was used by a china clay company in Devon for many years. It had taken over the job, from a 10 R–B dragline, of building up the sides of a large mica dam into which waste products were allowed to settle, while allowing the filtered water to be set free or recycled for further use in the china clay production process.

Above: **A Poclain MC100** loading a lorry on a demolition site in 1972.

Centre right: **This front shovel Poclain RC200** is loading a Berliet haul-truck in a sand and gravel operation in France around 1973.

Right: **The HC300** from Poclain was a sign that things were getting bigger, with only the big 1000 to come.

Left: The Poclain EC1000, weighing in at 142 tons and powered by General Motors 8V 71 engines giving 852hp (SAE). When first introduced in the 1970s it was one of the most powerful excavators of its kind.

Below: This EC1000 with front shovel equipment is loading a Euclid R45 dump truck in a Devon quarry and has probably taken over from a cable shovel during the late 1970s. Because of the impact such large hydraulic excavators have had over the last two decades many cable type face shovels have been either scrapped or put on to drop ball duties.

Below right: This Caterpillar 225 crawler hydraulic excavator is one of three very successful early models — the 215, 225 and 245. More recent Caterpillar models include the 5-wheel mounted models from 14 to 22.5 tons in weight and 29 crawler types from 7.4 tons to around 70 tons. Like all the latest high-tech hydraulic excavators they are available with a vast variety of attachments including buckets, grapples, nibblers, hydraulic hammers or picks, and scabblers, so they are now able to break up steel-reinforced concrete with relative ease, for example in the clearing of the massive freeway and interstate highways destroyed in the **California earthquake of late 1993.**

Left: This little Russian hydraulic excavator is one of a very wide range produced in their factories and exported to Bulgaria, Hungary and other Eastern European countries in fairly large numbers.

Below: This is a John Deere 410 digger/loader which achieved very large sales particularly in the USA and Canada, while the John Deere 1010 and 2010 crawler loaders fitted with the 95 backhoe were far more popular in Britain throughout the 1960s.

Left: This is the *original* RH25 from O & K on front shovel duties. It is using a 4 in 1 bullclam bucket to load a Faun haul-truck on a large earthmoving contract.

Right: Allis-Chalmers wheel loader 545–B or 605–B models are often sold with the matching CM–650 backhoe. These machines have served the Royal Engineers regiment of the British Army for many years. This photograph was taken during the 1960s before Allis–Chalmers' reorganisation during which they joined forces with Fiat of Italy then Hitachi of Japan.

Rear-mounted diggers occasionally turn up in the strangest places, including on the backs of Land Rovers, Mercedes, Unimogs, on the rear of farm tractors and elsewhere.

Below: This Poclain GC120 backhoe is working on a South Devon sea defence contract in July 1967.

Above: **J. I. Case (now Case-Poclain)** were one of the first manufacturers to introduce the hydraulically extending dipper arm on to digger/loaders. Known as the Extendahoe it was a valuable tool for contractors wishing to reach those parts others could not. The idea has since been taken up by other manufacturers.

Left: A standard J. I. Case 580F digger/loader from the 1960s.

Below: This little Case skid-steer loader is using a Case D100 hydraulic excavator attachment to add to its versatility.

Right: This Russian hydraulic excavator from 1969 has a front-mounted bulldozer blade in place of the usual loader, while the digger bucket has more of the appearance of a cable shovel type complete with a detachable trapdoor.

Below right: This Track-Marshall crawler loader fitted with a rear-mounted digger in the 1970s is similar to the machines made by Bristol Tractors, who once produced the Bristol Taurus and Europa crawler loaders which were also available with rear-mounted diggers. Bristol was eventually bought out by the Marshall Group, though eventually both were lost to the industry, which is sad, for a company such as Track-Marshall of Gainsborough, Lincolnshire, could be proud of having built some of the finest traction engines and steam rollers made in the early years of this century. They then turned to the production of diesel wheel and crawler tractors and road rollers.

Left: The Smalley 5 was one of the very first 360° slew mini-diggers when it first appeared in 1960, designed and built by a family-run firm from Bourne in Lincolnshire. Richard Smalley has built on his worldwide reputation for quality excavators and is now exporting newer models to North America, Finland and even to Japan.

The original idea was to produce a small machine to take away the painstaking task of digging graves. Very soon it was realised that, with their compactness, they were able to dig footings for house extensions without doing damage to the existing buildings and with minimal damage to the surrounding areas such as lawns and driveways. It was very quickly accepted by plant hirers and builders throughout Britain and abroad. The prototype was launched officially as the RSE mini-digger at Lincoln Show in June 1963. Their first enquiry was in the form of a letter from the then Austin Morris motor manufacturer over the use of the title 'mini' which was a registered trade name, so the Smalley excavator was renamed the 360 (in view of its ability to revolve fully). The first machine incorporated a BSA petrol engine and sold for £685. Almost all of the early machines were sold for export to Switzerland, Hawaii and Finnish Lapland. Smalley were, however, to replace the petrol engines with Lister SR1 diesels as it was found to be too easy for petrol to be pilfered from sites for use in cars.

Below: The Link-Belt Speeder hydraulic excavator model LS–4500 is one of the machines manufactured by a North American company (which also had factories in Italy, Mexico and Japan) whose previous business was the production of a range of cable-operated cranes and excavators. Many of the most successful hydraulic excavator manufacturers had no such experience to call on, as the hydraulic market was their first entry into excavator production, while others had made other types of earthmoving equipment such as scrapers, bulldozers and graders. This machine is working in Alabama, USA, during the early 1970s.

Above: **This Link-Belt Speeder LS-5000 is working in its home country of Italy during the 1970s. It was manufactured in Milan.**

Right: **This Weserhutte hydraulic wheel-mounted excavator on grab duties during the 1980s is from a company who produced their first steam shovel in Germany in 1908.**

Above: **A model 981 front-shovel from Liebher of France and Germany.**

Right: **The model HW75, from Weserhutte Otto Wolff on tracks during the 1980s.**

Below: **The Weserhutte HW130 is here using a bullclam front shovel bucket to load a dump truck in Germany in the 1980s.**

Continuous Excavators

L arge water-borne dredgers were constructed for the building of harbours and canals and for the mining of tin, gold and other minerals in the mid-19th century.

Towards the end of the 1800s, the same principles were applied to land-based excavators for work on canals, levees, excavation of chalk and clays for the production of cement, bricks, etc, and of iron-ore, lignite coal and other minerals.

Among one of the earliest companies to design and construct such machines was Backau R. Wolf of Germany.

In 1863 Wolf constructed the first of their dredgers, followed by many after the turn of the century; the first, in 1907, going to the brown coal mining area of the Rhine. Early machines of this type were similar to the early single-bucket excavators in that they ran on railway lines and were steam-powered, though by the early 20th century electric power became more popular for these large machines.

The early machines emptied their buckets at the top of the boom on to a chute, which in turn discharged the material into railway wagons for transportation to the disposal point. Large-scale conveyor systems replaced these chutes so that the spoil could be taken directly from the excavator to the disposal point.

Ladder type excavators were used extensively on the huge Panama Canal and Suez Canal projects, while in England they were also used to construct the batter on the Manchester Ship Canal.

The 1907 Backau-Wolf machines were equipped with twin passage hoppers, enabling them to load two trains passing behind the excavator, resulting in continuous production. Many of these machines were fitted with buckets of 300 litres capacity.

In 1927, Backau-Wolf designed the first successful bucket–chain slewing dredger. This machine could be used to remove overburden and coal, either with the bucket ladder at a high level or a deep level.

As early as 1926 a slewing spreader was in use with a boom length of 50m and a capacity of 1,000cu m/hour. This allowed for total control of the dump area, spreading the overburden evenly, without it piling up in one place and having to be pushed over the edge by bulldozers.

In 1933, Backau-Wolf started work on producing its first slewing, crawler-track-mounted machines.

In 1938 the biggest bucket-chain excavator in the world was produced. With an operating weight of 2,500 tons, it had 38 buckets each of 1,500 litres capacity. Installed electric power was 2,500kW.

The first bucket-wheel excavator was delivered by Backau-Wolf in 1941.

BUCKET-WHEEL SYSTEMS

These continuous-bucket excavators were developed in the latter half of the 19th century by companies such as Orenstein & Koppel Lubecker (O & K Lubecker Maschinenbau) and Backau-Wolf, both from Germany, the Boulet Company of France and A. F. Smulders in England.

These machines were originally powered by steam engines and were mounted on rail lines. The earliest of these excavators merely emptied the chain of buckets on to a chute or into a hopper from which the material could be discharged into railway trucks or horse-drawn carts. Eventually the conveyor belt was used to take material directly to the disposal point or to perform the task of loading the trucks.

Later machines were electrically powered or were driven by early oil engines. They were particularly popular with the canal engineers as they were able to cut the batter required along the sides of the excavation after the steam shovels had removed the bulk of excavated material. Such machines were used on the huge Panama Canal project and along the Manchester Ship Canal.

Others were widely used in the extraction of clays, chalk and gravels used in the production of cement, particularly in the Kent area of Southeast England, while ladder excavators were used in the ironstone mining industries of the Midlands.

The booms of these excavators were raised and lowered using cables, which were operated from a winch situated on the excavator. Backau R. Wolf made its first iron steam dredge in 1863, though it was after the turn of the century that full scale production of ladder type dredgers began. The first big bucket-chain dredger was delivered to the brown coal fields along the River Rhine in 1907. It was feasible for it to load two trains running on two sets of railway tracks beneath the excavator, by utilising an alternating chute, thereby enabling production to continue without having to break while waiting for trains to arrive. It was fitted with a mobile counter-weight which automatically balanced the constant shifting of the centre of gravity while it was working.

The rail-mounted machine was equipped with

Above: **This little bucket-wheel excavator is thought to be of German origin, possibly Weserhutte, and is at work in the Devon ball clay industry in the late 1950s/early 1960s. It was built under licence by Strachen & Henshaw of Bristol, England.**

bogies which could adhere to the track curves free of any constraint. Dredgers of this type were often made with buckets of 300 litres capacity each.

In 1927, Backau R. Wolf built the first bucket-chain slewing dredger, which could be used effectively to remove overburden and excavate the coal with its boom operating in either a high position for loading above ground or as a deep dredger for excavating well below ground level. With the use of conveyor belts to replace the trains for removing the overburden to the dumps, it was as early as 1926 that the first slewing spreader with a full 50m boom and a capacity of 1,000cu m/hour was put to work.

The first crawler-mounted ladder excavator from Backau R. Wolf was unveiled in 1933.

Nevertheless, bucket-chain excavators continued to be produced for some years, due largely to the effects the war had on the German companies' facilities.

The next large bucket-chain excavator, with a service weight of 3,300 tons, 44 buckets each of 2,000 litres capacity and 4,250kW of electric power was later built, but was not delivered under the management of Backau-Wolf, due to a move from the original factory in the Magdeburg area to Grevenbroich in 1947 as part of restructuring after the effects of the war.

During this time a new track-laying system was designed by Backau-Wolf for use on its latest large-scale excavators and giant spreaders. The truly 'track-laying' crawler was able to curve its way around the site. When the track is laid out in front of the huge machines, the belt can be gradually curved into the desired direction. With sets of crawlers of 55m in length and a total track surface of 320sq m, this was an industry first.

The above system was used on the latest bucket-wheel excavator of 3,900 tons, a capacity of 6,050cu m/hr, bucket volume of 2,250 litres, each with 10 buckets on the wheel. The cutting height of the wheel is 38m, it has a dredging depth of 5m and installed electrical power of 6,000kW. Other such excavators produced by Backau-Wolf include bunker dredgers, ash dredgers and chalk excavators.

Other German companies producing very large bucket-wheel excavators over many years have included Orenstein & Koppel (O & K), Krupp Weserhutte and Siemens, and Takraf, while similar machines were produced in France by Boulet. In the USA, Bucyrus-Erie and General Dynamics (Kobe) are among the leaders in this field.

Ruston-Hornsby and Ruston-Bucyrus have produced bucket-ladder dredgers and continuous excavators for special applications.

The Russians too were builders of large bucket-wheel systems, as they were of all other forms of excavators and earthmoving equipment.

Currently, very large bucket-wheel excavator systems (often consisting of numerous very large machines on the same site) are found mining lignite and brown coal in Germany, Greece, Russia, India, Australia and the USA. Bucket-wheels have been used in the mining of bauxite in North Africa, while in France such machines have been used to handle large quantities of sulphur, a by-product of natural gas deposits.

At Radar North opencast coal site in the north of England a bucket-wheel excavator helped walking draglines and electric shovels to remove the vast quantities of overburden above the important coal deposit in the 1950s and 1960s. This 300-ton excavator was supplied by Krupps, again of Germany,

The Anderson & Mavor Co of Glasgow, Scotland, were manufacturers of the model E10 bucket-wheel excavator as used on the excavation of a large reservoir in Buckinghamshire. They loaded Foden dump trucks and Caterpillar 619 and 631 motor scrapers with the mainly clay-based material.

In Rochester, Kent, a bucket-chain excavator with a cutting depth of 42m has been in operation for a leading cement manufacturer, while in Belgium a relatively small bucket-wheel excavator has been removing clay overburden and chalk with an output of 630cu m/hour.

Some of the largest of the bucket-wheels weigh well in excess of 12,000 tons.

At the bottom end of the scale, a small bucket-wheel machine went to work at the ball clay works in Newton Abbot in South Devon in the late 1950s or 1960s. Although no records of the make or model exist, it closely resembled the small Weserhutte machines. It is in enormous contrast to the model 6320 by Backau-Wolf, which has an hourly capacity of 10,400cu m and a daily output of 200,000cu m.

Below: **A little crawler-mounted machine loading one of the dozens of Muir-Hill dumpers used by Messrs Watts, Blake & Bearne at their many clay pits.**
Notice that the excavator uses hydraulics to raise and lower the boom and discharge belt, while the bucket-wheel was powered by an electric motor driving a reduction gearbox system.

Above: **The Kobe W–5 wheel excavator was designed by Frank Kobe and was manufactured by General-Dynamics in the USA.** Kobe was involved in the design of these bucket-wheel excavators as far back as the 1940s when he engaged Bucyrus-Erie to produce the digging wheel and upper works, while the Marion Power Shovel Co produced the crawler frames and lower works. The W–5 is working at the Fidelity surface coal mine in Illinois, alongside a Bucyrus-Erie stripping shovel. The discharge belt is fully operational to the left, while the size of this excavator can be judged by the power shovel, trucks and cars in the foreground.

Above right: **This giant bucket-wheel excavator comes from Krupps in Germany.** It is doing a fine job of gnawing away at the sandstone overburden at an open pit coal mine in the USA.

Right: **The Anderson Mavor E10 bucket-wheel excavator was made by Mavor & Coulson Ltd of Glasgow, Scotland.** It is working here on a reservoir project in the south of England loading into Foden dump trucks and Caterpillar scrapers. The E10 was crawler-mounted and the perfect tool for excavating this clay face. The material is being used as fill for a seal wall in the reservoir.

Above left: A close-up of the bucket-wheel of the E10 excavator.

Centre left: The main frame and power unit of the E10 wheel excavator during construction.

Below left: The transverse engine compartment of the E10 wheel excavator.

Below: The operator's cab of the E10. This hydraulically-operated machine was as advanced as any similar machine coming out of German factories during the mid-1960s.

Above right: This Krupps bucket-wheel excavator is loading bottom-dump trailers.

Right: A Backau-Wolf type Sch Rs 175/0.5.10 bucket-wheel excavator in use at a Belgian cement works. Note the left and right cabins for improved operator visibility.

Above: **The Backau-Wolf type Sch Rs 625/3.21 bucket excavator** is one of the great many bucket-wheel excavators to have worked at this opencast lignite mine, the Ptolemais, near Athens in Greece.

Left: This large bucket-wheel machine was built by Orenstein & Koppel at their Lubeck works in Germany for yet another large open pit around 1966.

Below left: The vast coal reserves in the Australian continent are well known, with a huge assortment of walking draglines, electric mining shovels and large-scale hydraulic excavators still being erected on huge sites every year. They can be proud of having some of the largest mining shovels and draglines ever built. This is certainly one of the largest bucket-wheel excavators to be used during the mid to late 1960s. It is a Backau-Wolf Sch 1300/2.5 and was assembled for work on the Morwell Open Cut for the State Electricity Commission of Victoria.

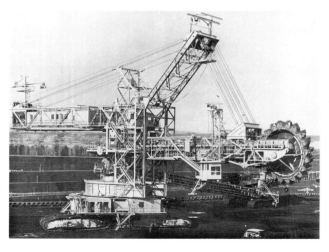

Above: **This large bucket-wheel system from Backau-Wolf of Germany has a capacity of 2,380 cubic m/hour and an excavating height of 28m.**

Right: **The type Sch Rs 2250/5.38 from Backau-Wolf is at home working in this German lignite mine, Frimmersdorf-West, for Roddergrube AG Kol-Bruhl.**

Below: **This Sch RS 650/4 .25 is working at the Megalopolis open-cut lignite mine at Thoknia for Public Power Corporation, Athens, Greece.**

Below right: **This is a rail-mounted bucket-wheel reclaimer with a capacity of 2,000 tons/hr in an ore**

Left: This bucket-wheel reclaimer is working on lignite, blending stockpiles at the Megalopolis power station in Greece. It can reclaim 970 tons/hour and is one of four identical machines on this project. All are crawler-mounted.

Below: This Backau-Wolf excavator is used in the advance cut for a lignite mine where it achieves an hourly output of 1540cu m. The volume of the bucket is 400 litres.

Right: This rail-mounted reclaimer is working in a storage bunker for a lignite power station. It has a capacity of 3180cu m/hour.

Below right: The machine featured in this photograph is a type Rs 3800/25.52 from Krupps. Notice that its bucket is the reverse of many of the machines so far featured — it digs underneath the boom with the wheel revolving towards the machine.

Above left: **The O & K wheel excavator in this photograph is clearly digging with its wheel revolving towards the machine. The enormity of the machine and its conveyor system is also evident.**

Left: **It is far from unusual for these huge lignite mines to employ two or more of these massive bucket-wheel systems. There are two in this photograph — the Krupps manufactured machine is in the foreground while another can just be seen off at the far right.**

Above: **This O & K SH400 hydraulic bucket-wheel excavator does a good job of separating the overburden from the mineral being mined in this open pit. The face shovel on the lower bench appears to have just enough height to reach the top of the bench.**

Below: Another view of the O & K Bucket Wheel Excavator (BWE), this time digging at ground level and stockpiling the spoil.

Above: **There are two of these 6,000-tons/hr stacker/reclaimers working for the Itabira iron-ore dressing plant in Brazil; both are from Backau-Wolf. Note its ability to draw material from the conveyors and to unload on to a stockpile.**

Below: **This is a conveyor stacker (or tripper as it is commonly known) working on a British opencast coal site. It was made in Germany by Krupps. Note the walking dragline at work in the background.**

Above: This huge crawler-mounted mobile tripper or spreader is handling all of the overburden being sent to it by the very large bucket-wheel excavators at the other end of this mine. It is not uncommon for the bucket wheel and the trippers to be as much as seven miles apart.

Below left: One of the more unusual continuous excavators was the Shale Planer. This one was made by Ruston's of Lincoln for the London Brick Company's King's Dyke operations near Stewartby, Bedfordshire. These specialist machines were first spotted at brickworks in the USA in 1922. By 1924 the first of this type was put to work in the Fletton Crown yard of the London Brick Company. Ruston & Hornsby began to market these machines in 1925. They used a continuous steel chain on which knives were fixed, drawn down across the face planing away the clay, which would then be taken away to the brick-making plant by conveyor belts. The capacity of the machine was 40-45cu yd/hr or enough to produce 12,000 to 15,000 bricks. Later machines were able to double the output of these earlier machines.

Three large crawler-mounted bucket-wheel excavators were supplied to remove overburden and tar sands from the Athabasca tar sands project in the north of Canada during the 1960s. The machine responsible for stripping the overburden was designed to load 240-ton-capacity dump trucks from a two-way chute at the rate of 40 seconds each, switching to the second truck instantaneously. The tar sand was loaded directly on to conveyor belts which delivered it to the separation plant some miles away from the main site.

All three machines were made in Germany for this harsh six months per year operation in temperatures often well below freezing.

LADDER TYPE EXCAVATORS

These were amongst the earliest of the steam-powered excavators, which were predominantly developed by German and French engineers. In Germany companies such as Orenstein & Koppel of Lubecker (O & K Lubecker Maschinenbau), Backau-Wolf, Krupps, and Weserhutte were the early pioneers in this form of excavating equipment. Other manufacturers have since become world leaders along with those early companies in the manufacture and sale of multi-bucket excavator systems, widely used in the open pit mining of gold, tin, lignite, coal, bauxite and phosphates throughout the world.

Many of the largest machines of this type weigh in excess of 12,000 tons, with one at least a little over 14,000.

They were originally developed for land use following the success of such machines equipped as dredgers for use on water. Ruston-Bucyrus and Bucyrus-Erie produced dredgers in the USA and Britain respectively for the mining of tin, gold and aluminium, and for baring rock and sands beneath the seas and estuaries.

Many ladder type excavators were used on the Panama Canal and the Suez Canal projects. Early ladder excavators were steam-powered and rail-mounted. As they did not have the benefits of the vulcanised rubber conveyor belts, they simply emptied their buckets on to chutes which could discharge the material into horse-drawn or rail-mounted dump cars.

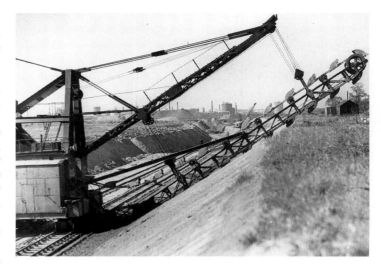

Top: **The ladder excavator in close-up. This excavator had progressed from steam to electric power, though it was still mounted on railway lines. It was in use for many years at the Midlands ironstone mines.**

Above: **The ladder excavator seen from a distance, including the discharge conveyor to the left of the picture. Note its two sets of railway lines.**

Top right: **This photograph of a large O & K ladder type excavator was taken in September 1961. Note that these comparatively recent machines were still mounted on rail lines, though they were able to discharge on to conveyor systems capable of moving the excavated material many miles to the discharge point.**

Right: **This huge machine is one of the Krupps ladder type excavators, the type RS 1000 x 28. Note the second machine in the background on the left of the picture. It is believed that no less than four of these machines were in operation at this Italian mine site.**

TRENCHERS

Although most of the ladder type dredgers and land excavators had been made by German companies, ladder and bucket-wheel trenchers were in the main produced by USA companies from 1900 — companies such as the Buckeye Manufacturing Co of Anderson, Indiana, the Cleveland Trencher Co, of Cleveland, Ohio, Barber-Greene of Aurora, Illinois, and Parsons.

Barber-Greene

Harry H. Barber was born in Freeport, Illinois, USA, on 18 January 1878. W. B. Greene was born on 4 September 1886 in Lisle, DuPage County, Illinois. Both were of pioneer stock and both graduated from the University of Illinois as Mechanical Engineers (Barber 1907, Greene 1908).

While helping out on their family farms, they realised the difficulties in handling large amounts of material, grain fertilizers, etc together with the isolation resulting from the bad roads linking the farms to the market towns.

Harry Barber found employment with the Link-Belt Co (who manufactured cranes and excavators), though this was only during the summer recess from college. On graduation he joined the Stephens-Adamson Manufacturing Company of Aurora, Illinois, together with a classmate, Earl Stearns.

Greene joined the Robins Co in 1908, eventually Hewitt-Robins, which pioneered the conveyor belt.

Both men became acutely aware of the importance of mechanisation to the material-handling industries. They gained valuable knowledge of how industries were served by their employers' products. In addition, they came to realise how other industries could be served by similar products. One was the retail coal industry, where bags were both weighed and filled by hand, whereas, with a degree of ingenuity, this task could be performed better by machine.

It was in 1916 that both men decided to put their new ideas into operation.

Both Barber and Greene had done work for the same company, Stephens-Adamson, for a few years when they approached a local engineering concern (W. S. Frazier & Co) to provide manufacturing facilities for around 20 of their own proposals, all designed to dispense with hand shovels, wheelbarrows, etc.

The company were pleased to have been asked to provide what help they could, and as subcontractors they were soon manufacturing conveyor belts mounted on spoked iron wheels, and bucket loaders which could pick up coal, grain and gravels from the stockpile and, by means of a chute, direct the material into wagons, lorries or bags. The first of these was designed in 1916 and manufactured the following year.

In 1922 their first unsuccessful trencher model appeared, mounted on a bucket loader chassis, which appeared not to be strong enough to cope with the pressures put upon it when working in hard ground. However, after improvements and modifications the first production model was released in 1923. Over the coming few years many of these machines found favour in the newly developing state of Florida, where hard coral rocks were being encountered and dealt with by the Barber-Greene trenchers. New crawler-mounted bucket loaders found favour with the retail coal companies, who at a stroke could load lorries straight from the stockpile with ease.

One of the most successful Barber-Greene ditchers was the model 44–C, made from 1927 to 1957. It had a vertical boom, and found itself in service for both civilian and military users for some years.

An experimental excavator was tested in 1927 which had four vertically actuating endless bucket belts and was able to move thousands of cubic yards of material with relative ease, while loading via conveyors into trucks. It was not, however, to be a commercial success, probably because of the availability of BV loaders, scrapers and excavators on a large scale, which left little room for this all-new idea.

Other applications for their belt loaders included that of snow clearing, which in the harsh winters of the USA and Canada attracted the attention of the many local utilities. These included those in Connecticut, where in 1938 a model 38–D was used extensively, while the model 538–A found favour on the streets of Port Chester, New York in 1948.

The model 750 mobile ditcher was produced for use by the USA Army Corps of Engineers. Sixty-four were built mounted on a special wheel tractor chassis.

The model 777, introduced in 1960, was claimed to be the largest and most powerful full crawler 'bucket-wheel' ditcher. It was able to excavate in excess of 12 tons/minute while depositing the spoil, as with all such trenchers, neatly alongside the trench.

ENDLESS-BUCKET TRENCHERS

These unique-looking machines often pre-date many of the best known single-bucket excavator manufacturers as many were developed as early as 1900. The most successful manufacturers of these machines were nevertheless small in number, and in almost all cases, were subsidiaries of manufacturers of the single-bucket excavator. The Parsons Trenching Machine Co was a subsidiary of Koehring, which became one of the world leaders in cable and hydraulic single-bucket excavators, while Buckeye had become linked with the Page Manufacturing Co, producers of some of the most successful walking draglines and themselves a pioneering company in that field. Barber-Greene, famous for their tarmac-laying machines, quarry plant and conveyors were also manufacturers of multi-bucket excavators. Cleveland Trencher, like the previously listed companies, is yet another American manufacturer.

John Allen of Oxford topped the list of British manufacturers. Initially they manufactured under a licensing agreement with Parsons of the USA.

The following photographs depict various multi-bucket trenchers from manufacturers in the USA, Britain and Russia.

Above: **A Buckeye traction ditcher from around 1918.**

Left: **This Buckeye model 301 from 1948 is the wheel type of trencher.**

Above: **The model 120 from Buckeye is a ladder trencher from the early 1950s.**

Below: **This Buckeye wheel ditcher model 306 is from 1950.**

Right: **This Cleveland wheel trencher is hard at work for the Royal Engineers regiment of the British Army.**

Right: **An Allen 12/18 trencher with ladder type boom at work for the Royal Engineers regiment in the 1950s. It was, however, in production from the late 1920s.**

Below: **This Barber-Greene vertical boom trencher is working for the British Army.**

Above: **This Russian ladder trencher is a model ETY–201. It** differed from many of the previous machines in that the operator was supplied with a cab. On many of the Allen and other Western trenchers they were not even given the luxury of a seat. The operator had just a small plate on which to stand to operate the machine.

Below: **This Russian ladder trencher is a model ETY–354.** The operator here is allowed the relative comfort of a seat and limited shelter.

Above right: **One of the very popular Barber-Greene TA–30 wheel ditchers made for MD Smith Construction Company in the USA.**

Right: **Barber-Greene's unique vertical boom ditcher** is represented here by the model TT–35. Note that the boom is able to operate at an angle similar to that on ladder trenchers.

Above: **As a result of Barber-Greene's continuing research and development programme we have this unique continuous excavator from 1927. Due to the popularity of shovels and universal excavators this machine made much less impact upon the industry than had been hoped. Ironically, similar machines are now being produced at an alarming rate by both** USA and German manufacturers, particularly for the continuous loading of surface coal and other minerals.

Below: A more recent development by Barber-Greene was this continuous wheel excavator produced from around 1966 and marketed for some 10 years.